Target
Get back on track 5

AQA GCSE (9–1)
English Literature

Unseen Poetry

David Grant

Pearson

Published by Pearson Education Limited, 80 Strand, London, WC2R 0RL.
www.pearsonschoolsandfecolleges.co.uk

Text © Pearson Education Ltd 2017
Typeset by Tech-Set Ltd, Gateshead

The right of David Grant to be identified as author of this work has been asserted by him in accordance with the Copyright, Designs and Patents Act 1988.

First published 2017

20 19 18
10 9 8 7 6 5 4 3 2

British Library Cataloguing in Publication Data
A catalogue record for this book is available from the British Library

ISBN 978 1 292 23011 5

Printed in Italy by LEGO S.p.A

Acknowledgments
Pages 2, 4, 5, 6: 'Tea' from *Love Poems* by Carol Ann Duffy. Copyright © 2010. Used by permission of Pan Macmillan; pages 10, 11, 12, 13: 'maggie and milly and molly and may' from *Complete Poems, 1904–1962* by e e Cummings, edited by George J. Firmage. Copyright © 1956, 1984, 1991 by the Trustees of the e e Cummings Trust. Used by permission of Liveright Publishing Corporation; page 18: 'Otherwise' from *Collected Poems* by Jane Kenyon. Copyright © 2005 by the Estate of Jane Kenyon. Reprinted with the permission of The Permissions Company, Inc. on behalf of Graywolf Press, Minneapolis, Minnesota. www.graywolfpress.org; pages 26, 27, 28: 'City Lilacs' from *Glad of These Times* by Helen Dunmore. Copyright © 2007. Reproduced with permission of Bloodaxe Books. www.bloodaxebooks.com; pages 34, 35, 36: 'The Round' from *Passing Through: The Later Poems – New and Selected* by Stanley Kunitz. Copyright © 1985. Used by permission of W. W. Norton & Company, Inc.; pages 42, 43, 44, 47: 'Postcard' by Beatrice Garland. Copyright © Beatrice Garland; pages 50, 51, 52, 54: 'Strawberries' from *New Selected Poems* by Edwin Morgan. Copyright © 2000. Used by permission of Carcanet Press; pages 58, 59, 60: 'My Grandfather's Garden' from *The Blue Book* by Owen Sheers (Seren, 2000); pages 58, 59, 60: 'Poem' from *The Shout: Selected Poems* by Simon Armitage. Copyright © Simon Armitage; page 74: 'Legend' from *Five Fields* by Gillian Clarke. Copyright © 1998. Used by permission of Carcanet Press; page 75: 'Mother to Son' from *The Collected Poems of Langston Hughes* by Langston Hughes, edited by Arnold Rampersad with David Roessel, Associate Editor. Copyright © 1994 by the Estate of Langston Hughes. Used by permission of Alfred A. Knopf, an imprint of the Knopf Doubleday Publishing Group, a division of Penguin Random House LLC. All rights reserved; Reprinted by permission of Harold Ober Associates Incorporated. Copyright © 1994 by the Estate of Langston Hughes; page 76: 'A Letter in October' from *Weather Central* by Ted Kooser, © 1994. Reprinted by permission of the University of Pittsburgh Press.

Note from the publisher
Pearson has robust editorial processes, including answer and fact checks, to ensure the accuracy of the content in this publication, and every effort is made to ensure this publication is free of errors. We are, however, only human, and occasionally errors do occur. Pearson is not liable for any misunderstandings that arise as a result of errors in this publication, but it is our priority to ensure that the content is accurate. If you spot an error, please do contact us at resourcescorrections@pearson.com so we can make sure it is corrected.

Contents

1 Tackling an unseen poem

Get started — 1

1 How do I read a poem and check my understanding? — 3
2 How do I identify the key ideas in a poem? — 4
3 How do I identify the poet's intention? — 5
   Get back on track — 6

2 Developing a personal response

Get started — 9

1 How can I develop my response to the ideas in the poem? — 11
2 How can I identify the mood of a poem? — 12
3 How do I know whether my personal response is the right response? — 13
   Get back on track — 14

3 Exploring structure

Get started — 17

1 How do I explore how a poem develops? — 19
2 How do I explore a poem's structural features? — 20
3 How do I comment on structure? — 21
   Get back on track — 22

4 Exploring the poet's language choices

Get started — 25

1 How do I identify language choices that create a specific effect? — 27
2 How do I know what effect the poet is trying to create? — 28
3 How do I comment on the poet's language choices? — 29
   Get back on track — 30

5 Exploring poetic devices

Get started — 33

1 How do I explore sound devices in a poem? — 35
2 How do I explore the imagery in a poem? — 36
3 How do I comment on the poet's use of poetic devices? — 37
   Get back on track — 38

6 Exploring the poet's use of form

Get started — 41

1 How do I explore form? — 43
2 How do I explore rhythm and rhyme? — 44
3 How do I comment on the poet's use of form? — 45
   Get back on track — 46

7 Writing about one poem

Get started — 49

1 How do I annotate a poem? — 51
2 How do the elements of a poem work together? — 52
3 How do I structure my response? — 53
   Get back on track — 54

8 Comparing poems

Get started — 57

1 How do I plan my comparison? — 59
2 How do I develop my comparison? — 60
3 How do I structure my comparison? — 61
   Get back on track — 62

9 Expressing your ideas clearly and precisely

Get started — 65

1 How do I choose vocabulary which expresses my ideas precisely? — 67
2 How can I link my ideas to express them more clearly? — 68
3 How can I extend my sentences to develop my ideas more fully? — 69
   Get back on track — 70

More practice texts — 73

Answers — 77

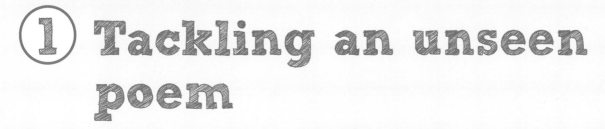

① Tackling an unseen poem

This unit will help you to read, understand and explore an unseen poem. The skills you will build are to:

- read and develop an understanding of an unseen poem
- identify the key ideas in the poem
- identify the poet's intention – the impact the poet wants their poem to have on a reader.

In the exam you will face questions like the one below. This is about the poem on the next page. At the end of the unit you will **write one paragraph** in response to this question.

Exam-style question

In 'Tea', how does the poet present the speaker's feelings?   **(24 marks)**

Before you respond to the question you will work through three key questions in the **skills boosts** to help you tackle an unseen poem.

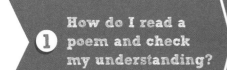

| ① How do I read a poem and check my understanding? | ② How do I identify the key ideas in a poem? | ③ How do I identify the poet's intention? |

Read the poem on the next page. In Paper 2, Section C of your English Literature exam, you will write about one unseen poem, then compare it with another unseen poem.

As you read the poem, think about: ✓

| who is talking to whom | what they are saying | why they are saying it. |

Tea 🖉

I like pouring your tea, lifting
the heavy pot, and tipping it up,
so the fragrant liquid streams in your china cup.

Or when you're away, or at work,
5   I like to think of your cupped hands as you sip,
as you sip, of the faint half-smile of your lips.

I like the questions – sugar? – milk? –
and the answers I don't know by heart, yet,
for I see your soul in your eyes, and I forget.

10   Jasmine, Gunpowder, Assam, Earl Grey, Ceylon,
I love tea's names. Which tea would you like? I say
but it's any tea for you, please, any time of day,

as the women harvest the slopes
for the sweetest leaves, on Mount Wu-Yi,
15   and I am your lover, smitten, straining your tea.

Carol Ann Duffy

(1) Underline (A) any words or phrases in the poem that you do not recognise or understand.

(2) You can often work out the meaning of unfamiliar words or phrases by looking at words or phrases around them. Look at the circled phrases from the poem, below.

A   Jasmine, Gunpowder, Assam, Earl Grey, Ceylon,
I love tea's names. Which tea would you like? I say

B   as the women harvest the slopes
for the sweetest leaves, on Mount Wu-Yi,

(a) Note 🖉 down alongside each circled phrase everything that you can work out about its meaning.

(b) Underline (A) other words or phrases around them that helped you.

(3) Look again at any of the words or phrases you underlined in the poem because you did not recognise or understand them. Note 🖉 down alongside them what you can work out about their meaning by looking at other words and phrases around them.

> If you're still not sure about an idea or a phrase or a word in an unseen poem, work around it – focus on what you <u>do</u> understand.

How do I read a poem and check my understanding?

When you first read a poem that you have never seen before, you need to read it carefully and be confident that you have understood what it is about.

Read the poem 'Tea' on page 2 again.   Always read the poem **twice**.

One way to develop your understanding of a poem is to picture in your mind what is being described.

1 **a** Read the first verse of the poem. Picture the scene in your mind, then draw 🖉 that picture in the space below. You can use:

- stick people with expressions on their faces
- speech bubbles and thought bubbles
- labels to make your drawing clearer.

b Look at your drawing. Write 🖉 **one** sentence, summarising the poem.

....

....

c Re-read the poem, checking each line and each verse against your summary of the poem. Is your summary accurate? Annotate 🖉 your summary with any changes needed to make it more accurate.

d Annotating the poem on page 2, circle Ⓐ **two** key words or phrases that support, and help to explain, your summary.

2 How do I identify the key ideas in a poem?

Focusing on the writer's vocabulary choices, the title and the poem's final line, can help you to identify, and develop your understanding of, the poem's key ideas.

① The **title** of a poem and its **final line** often give clear clues to the key ideas in the poem.

Look at the title and the final line of the poem 'Tea' on page 2. What do you think are the key ideas in the poem?

a Note 🖉 the key ideas below, using just **one** or **two** words to sum up each idea.

....

....

b Label 🖉 each key idea you have identified **A, B, C**, etc.

② Now look at all the nouns, verbs, adjectives and adverbs the writer has used in the poem.

✓ 🖉	✓ 🖉	✓ 🖉	✓ 🖉
answers	half-smile	milk	straining
Assam	hands	Mount Wu-Yi	streams
Ceylon	harvest	names	sugar
china	heart	please	sweetest
cup	heavy	pot	tea
cupped	Jasmine	pouring	think
day	know	questions	time
Earl Grey	leaves	say	tipping
eyes	lifting	see	women
faint	lips	sip	work
forget	liquid	slopes	
fragrant	love	smitten	
Gunpowder	lover	soul	

a Tick ✓ each word that is linked to the key ideas you noted in question **①** **a** above.

b Look at all the words you have ticked. Label 🖉 each one with the letter you gave to the relevant key idea in question **①** **b** above.

③ a Now highlight 🖉 all the pronouns (e.g. 'I', 'you', 'he', 'she', etc...) that the writer has used in the poem and list 🖉 them below in the order in which they occur.

....

b Look at all the pronouns you noted above. Which one does the poet use most? Which is the next most common? What does this suggest about the poem's key ideas? Write 🖉 **two** or **three** sentences on paper summing up your understanding of the poem's key ideas.

③ How do I identify the poet's intention?

Identifying the poet's intention will help you to develop your understanding and explore how the poet has tried to achieve that intention.

intention: the impact that the writer wants the text to have on the reader

① Identifying the characters in a poem – all the people the poet writes about and the ways in which these characters interact – can help your understanding of the poem and the poet's intention. Look again at 'Tea' on page 2.

   a Who are the people in this poem? Label 🖉 the diagram below.

   b Who is talking to whom? Add 🖉 **one** or **more** speech bubbles to the diagram with a summary of what they are saying.

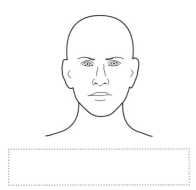

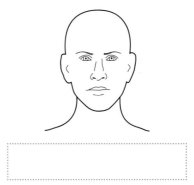

② Look carefully at these key lines from the poem.

> I like the questions – sugar? – milk? –
> and the answers I don't know by heart, yet,
> for I see your soul in your eyes, and I forget.

What impressions does the poet want the reader to have about each of the people in the poem and what they are talking about? Add 🖉 your ideas to the diagram above.

③ Review the diagram above. What are your thoughts, feelings and impressions of these people? How do you think the writer wants you to think and feel about them? Write 🖉 **one** or **two** sentences summing up your ideas about the writer's intention.

....

....

....

....

Tackling an unseen poem

When you begin to tackle an unseen poem, aim to:

- 'picture the poem': imagine the scene or events the poet is writing about
- look at the title, the final line, and the writer's vocabulary choices, to help you identify the key ideas in the poem
- think about your impressions of the people and ideas in the poem to help you identify the writer's intention.

Now look at this exam-style question you saw at the start of the unit.

Exam-style question

In 'Tea', how does the poet present the speaker's feelings? **(24 marks)**

(1) Circle (A) the key words in the exam-style question above: what are you being asked to write about?

(2) Now look at one student's planning notes, written in response to the question above.

A	I like pouring your tea	*The speaker likes making tea for the person she loves.*
B	when you're away, or at work I like to think of your cupped hands as you sip	*She often thinks about this person when they're not there.*
C	the answers I don't know by heart, yet	*She hasn't known this person long but expects them to be together for a long time.*
D	it's any tea for you, please, any time of day	*This person loves tea.*
E	Jasmine, Gunpowder, Assam, Earl Grey, Ceylon	*She loves the names of different teas.*
F	I am your lover, smitten, straining your tea	*She has very strong feelings for this person.* *She enjoys doing things that make this person happy.*
G	I see your soul in your eyes, and I forget.	*Her feelings are so strong that they stop her thinking about anything else.*

Which of these ideas would you include in your response? Tick (✓) them.

Your turn!

You are now going to **write one paragraph** in response to the exam-style question, summarising the poem's key ideas and the writer's intention.

Exam-style question

In 'Tea', how does the poet present the speaker's feelings?   **(24 marks)**

1 Look back through all your work in this unit. Use the space below to note 🖉 all the thoughts and ideas you could include in your summary.

The key ideas in the poem	The impressions that the writer wants to give of the people in the poem

2 Which of the ideas you have noted are relevant to the exam-style question? Tick ✓ them.

3 Using your notes, write 🖉 **one** paragraph on paper in response to the exam-style question above, summarising the poem's key ideas and the writer's intention.

Review your skills

Check up

Review your response to the exam-style question on page 7. Tick ✓ the column to show how well you think you have done each of the following.

	Not quite ✓	Nearly there ✓	Got it! ✓
summarised the key ideas in the poem	☐	☐	☐
summarised the writer's intention	☐	☐	☐

Need more practice?

Here is another exam-style question, this time relating to 'When You Are Old' by William Butler Yeats, which can be found on page 73.

Exam-style question

In 'When You Are Old', how does the poet present the speaker's feelings?   (24 marks)

Write **one** paragraph in response to the exam-style question, **summarising** the poem's key ideas and the writer's intention. You'll find some suggested points to refer to in the Answers section.

Comparison practice

Here is another exam-style question relating to **both** 'Tea' by Carol Ann Duffy **and** 'When You Are Old' by William Butler Yeats.

Exam-style question

In both 'Tea' and 'When You Are Old' the speakers talk about love. What are the similarities and/or differences between the ways the poets present love?   (24 marks)

Write ✐ **one** or **two** paragraphs in response to the exam-style question, **comparing** the key ideas and the writers' intentions in 'Tea' and 'When You Are Old'.

How confident do you feel about each of these **skills?** Colour ✐ in the bars.

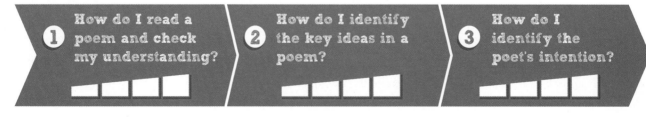

1 How do I read a poem and check my understanding?

2 How do I identify the key ideas in a poem?

3 How do I identify the poet's intention?

② Developing a personal response

This unit will help you to develop a personal response to an unseen poem. The skills you will build are to:

- develop your response to the ideas in an unseen poem
- identify and explore the mood of an unseen poem
- develop confidence in your response to an unseen poem.

In the exam you will face questions like the one below. This is about the poem on the next page. At the end of the unit you will **write two paragraphs** in response to this question.

Exam-style question

In 'maggie and milly and molly and may', how does the poet present the seaside?   **(24 marks)**

Before you tackle the question you will work through three key questions in the **skills boosts** to help you develop a personal response to the poem.

 ① How can I develop my response to the ideas in the poem? ② How can I identify the mood of a poem? ③ How do I know whether my personal response is the right response?

Read the poem on the next page. In Paper 2, Section C of your English Literature exam, you will write about one unseen poem.

As you read the poem, think about:

what happens at the seaside

your impressions of the seaside

your impressions of the characters in the poem.

maggie and milly and molly and may ✎

maggie and milly and molly and may
went down to the beach (to play one day)

and maggie discovered a shell that sang
so sweetly she couldn't remember her troubles, and

5   milly befriended a stranded star
whose rays five languid fingers were;

and molly was chased by a horrible thing
which raced sideways while blowing bubbles: and

may came home with a smooth round stone
10   as small as a world and as large as alone.

For whatever we lose (like a you or a me)
it's always ourselves we find in the sea

e e cummings

1 When you first read a poem, think about:
- **what** happens
- **when** and/or **where** it happens
- **who** is in the poem
- **how** the events, places and people in the poem are presented.

a   Imagine the scene described in the poem. What is the poem about? Note ✎ down all your ideas below.

b   Write ✎ **one** or **two** sentences summarising your ideas. You could begin your summary:

The poem is about...   The poem explores...   The poem focuses on...

1 How can I develop my response to the ideas in the poem?

When you have read a poem, read through it again, thinking about and responding to each idea and image it creates in your mind. Then, to help you develop your response, **think about how those ideas and images can be connected**.

(1) Look at the image created in the **first** stanza of the poem.

> maggie and milly and molly and may
> went down to the beach (to play one day)

What does this first image lead you to expect from the poem? Annotate the quotation above with your ideas.

(2) Now look at some more images and ideas taken from the poem.

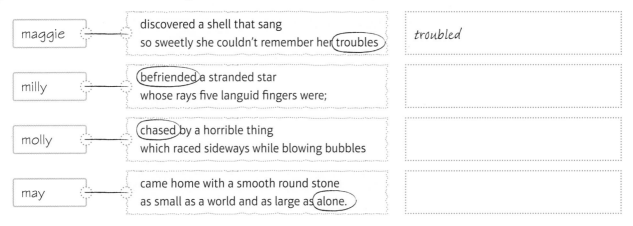

maggie	discovered a shell that sang so sweetly she couldn't remember her troubles	*troubled*
milly	befriended a stranded star whose rays five languid fingers were;	
molly	chased by a horrible thing which raced sideways while blowing bubbles	
may	came home with a smooth round stone as small as a world and as large as alone.	

Look carefully at what happens to each character in the poem and each of the words the poet has selected to describe those events. What might the poet be suggesting about each character? Note **one** or **two** words alongside each quotation. One idea has been suggested for you.

(3) Poems often connect very different ideas, settings, people or events to make you think about them in a different way.

What connections can you make between the ways in which the writer presents the setting, characters and events in the poem? Are there any strange or surprising connections?

Write **one** or **two** sentences explaining your ideas.

> Try comparing what the first stanza of the poem leads you to expect, with the rest of the poem.

....

....

....

2 How can I identify the mood of a poem?

Certain key words can create the mood of a poem.

> mood: the emotion, tone or atmosphere created in a text

When you think about the mood of a poem, or part of a poem:

• decide whether the mood is positive or negative

• try to think of a more specific word that describes the mood as precisely as possible.

For example, the mood might be:

positive

| optimistic | affectionate | comic | warm | contemplative | sympathetic | happy | excited |

negative

| pessimistic | gloomy | disturbing | unsettling | terrifying | cynical | angry | tense |

1 Think about the mood suggested at the **start** of the poem on page 10.

> maggie and milly and molly and may
>
> went down to the beach (to play one day)

a How would you describe the mood in this first stanza? How does the stanza make **you** feel? Note ✏ down **one** or **two** words to describe the mood as precisely as you can. You could choose from the ideas above, or use your own.

....

b Which words in the first stanza help to create the mood you have identified? Circle Ⓐ **one** or **two** of them.

2 Now look at another two stanzas from the poem.

> and molly was chased by a horrible thing
>
> which raced sideways while blowing bubbles: and
>
> may came home with a smooth round stone
>
> as small as a world and as large as alone.

> The mood of a poem can change as it develops, sometimes creating a surprising mixture of moods.

a How would you describe the mood in these stanzas? How do they make **you** feel? Note ✏ down **one** or **two** words that describe the mood or moods created in these stanzas as precisely as you can. You could choose from the ideas above, or use your own.

....

b Which words in these stanzas help to create the mood or moods you have identified? Circle Ⓐ **two** or **three** of them and label ✏ them with the mood or feeling they create..

③ How do I know whether my personal response is the right response?

A poem may be 'about' more than it first appears to be. A poem may describe a small event – but it may be the poet's intention to prompt big ideas in the reader. **Any** response that is supported by evidence, and shows that you have understood and responded to **some** or **all** of the ideas in the poem, will **always** be right.

① Look at some of these responses to the poem 'maggie and milly and molly and may' on page 10.

Response	✕	✓	Evidence
A The poem is about some children playing on a beach.	☐	☐	
B The poem explores how children respond differently to things they find at the seaside.	☐	☐	
C The poem is about how all children are individuals.	☐	☐	
D The poem explores the idea that childhood can be a difficult time in our lives.	☐	☐	
E The poem is about the ways in which the world can be both comforting and frightening.	☐	☐	

a For each response, note ✎ down a short quotation from the poem to support it. If you cannot find any relevant evidence, put a cross ✕ in the first check box next to the response instead.

b Which of the responses are most and least developed? Label ✎ them '**most**' and '**least**'.

c Which **one** of these responses do you agree with most strongly? Put a tick ✓ in the second check box alongside your chosen response.

② When you have developed your response to the parts of the poem you feel more confident about, you can try to develop a response to some of the more challenging parts of the poem.

> For whatever we lose (like a you or a me) ——————— How can we lose 'a you or a me'?
>
> it's always ourselves we find in the sea ——————— How can we 'find ourselves' in the sea?

a What might the poet be suggesting in the **final** stanza? Note ✎ down some possible ideas.

.... ☐

.... ☐

.... ☐

b Which of your ideas do you agree with most strongly? Tick ✓ them.

Developing a personal response

To develop a personal response to a poem, you need to:

- think about the ideas and images in the poem and try to find some connection between them
- identify the mood or moods created in the poem and consider how, and why, they change
- think about the bigger ideas the poet might be exploring in the poem
- most importantly, check you can support your response with evidence from the poem.

Now look at this exam-style question you saw at the start of the unit.

Exam-style question

In 'maggie and milly and molly and may', how does the poet present the seaside?   **(24 marks)**

Look at these paragraphs taken from two students' responses to the question.

Student A

The seaside is presented as somewhere that children play and can have fun. For example, Maggie finds a shell 'that sang' and Milly 'befriended' a starfish. These images create a positive mood and suggest that the seaside is a place where you can forget your 'troubles' and get closer to nature.

However, the seaside can also be a frightening place: Molly was 'chased by a horrible thing'. The poet does not say what this 'thing' was, but describing it as a 'thing' suggests what a strange and terrifying creature it was and how terrified a child might have been.

Student B

At the start of the poem, the words 'beach' and 'play' suggest that the children have gone to the seaside for a fun day out, but this idea changes as the poem develops. Although some of the images in the poem are positive, most have a negative side. Maggie has 'troubles', Milly 'befriended' a starfish, which could suggest she is lonely, and Molly is chased by 'a horrible thing'. The impression this creates is that children are all individuals who cope in different ways with different problems. It suggests that the seaside is a place where we 'find ourselves' because it shows us what we are really like.

	Student A	Student B	Neither
① a. Which student has developed their response by finding ways to connect the different ideas in the poem? ✓	☐	☐	☐
b. Which student has commented on the mood of the poem? ✓	☐	☐	☐
c. Which student has explored some of the bigger ideas in the poem? ✓	☐	☐	☐

Your turn!

You are now going to **write two paragraphs** in response to the exam-style question.

Exam-style question

In 'maggie and milly and molly and may', how does the poet present the seaside?   **(24 marks)**

① Before you start to plan your response, consider the key point in the question: how is the seaside presented in the poem? Think about:

(?) what happens at the beach   (?) how the children respond   (?) what this reveals about them

(?) the moods created in the poem   (?) bigger ideas the poet might be exploring

A ☐

B ☐

C ☐

D ☐

E ☐

a How is the seaside presented? Note ✎ down **five** key ideas in the poem in boxes A–E above.

b Add ✎ evidence to support each idea you have noted.

c What connections can you make between the ideas you noted? Draw ✎ lines linking any of the key ideas above that are connected. Annotate ✎ the lines to explain the connections.

d Review your ideas, evidence and connections. Tick ✓ those you will include in your writing.

② Now write ✎ **two** paragraphs on paper in response to the exam-style question.

Review your skills

Check up

Review your response to the exam-style question on page 15. Tick ✓ the column to show how well you think you have done each of the following.

	Not quite ✓	Nearly there ✓	Got it! ✓
identified connections between key ideas in the poem	☐	☐	☐
explored the moods created in the poem	☐	☐	☐
explored the bigger ideas in the poem	☐	☐	☐

Need more practice?

Here is another exam-style question, this time relating to 'Legend' by Gillian Clarke, which can be found on page 74.

Exam-style question

In 'Legend', how does the poet present the speaker's experience of a visit to the park in winter?

(24 marks)

Write ✐ **two** paragraphs in response to the exam-style question, **focusing on your personal response to the ideas in the poem**. You'll find some suggested points to refer to in the Answers section.

Comparison practice

Here is another exam-style question, relating to **both** 'maggie and milly and molly and may' by e e cummings **and** 'Legend' by Gillian Clarke.

Exam-style question

In both 'maggie and milly and molly and may' and 'Legend', childhood experiences are described. What are the similarities and/or differences between the ways the poets present childhood?

(8 marks)

Write ✐ **one** or **two** paragraphs in response to the exam-style question, **comparing** your personal response to the ideas in 'maggie and milly and molly and may' with your personal response to the ideas in 'Legend'. You'll find some suggested points to refer to in the Answers section.

How confident do you feel about each of these **skills?** Colour ✐ in the bars.

1 How can I develop my response to the ideas in the poem?

2 How can I identify the mood of a poem?

3 How do I know whether my personal response is the right response?

Analyse the language, form and structure used by a writer to create meanings and effects (AO2)

③ Exploring structure

This unit will help you to explore the poet's use of structure in an unseen poem. The skills you will build are to:

- track the structure and development of ideas in a poem
- analyse the impact of structural features in a poem
- comment effectively on structure.

In the exam you will face questions like the one below. This is about the poem on the next page. At the end of the unit you will **write two paragraphs** in response to this question.

Exam-style question

In 'Otherwise', how does the poet present the speaker's feelings about her life?   **(24 marks)**

Before you tackle the question you will work through three key questions in the **skills boosts** to help you explore the poem's structure.

 1 How do I explore how a poem develops?

 2 How do I explore a poem's structural features?

 3 How do I comment on structure?

Read the poem on the next page. In Paper 2, Section C of your English Literature exam, you will write about one unseen poem, then compare it with another unseen poem.

As you read the poem, think about: ⊘

what you learn about the speaker's life	how you feel about the speaker's life	how the speaker feels about her life.
☐	☐	☐

Otherwise

I got out of bed
on two strong legs.
It might have been
otherwise. I ate
5   cereal, sweet
milk, ripe, flawless
peach. It might
have been otherwise.
I took the dog uphill
10   to the birch wood.
All morning I did
the work I love.

At noon I lay down
with my mate. It might
15   have been otherwise.
We ate dinner together
at a table with silver
candlesticks. It might
have been otherwise.
20   I slept in a bed
in a room with paintings
on the walls, and
planned another day
just like this day.
25   But one day, I know,
it will be otherwise.

Jane Kenyon

(1) What do you think the speaker in this poem will do tomorrow? Write ✎ a list below.

....
....
....
....
....
....
....
....
....
....
....

How do I explore how a poem develops?

Tracking the ideas or events described in a poem will help you explore the ways in which it develops.

(1) Some of the methods a poet may use to give a poem structure include:

Time	The poem tracks an idea or experience over a period of seconds, minutes, hours, days, or years.	*For example, a poem might compare the past and the present, or describe the present and imagine the future.*	
Movement	The poem moves through a setting, observing and recording it.	*For example, a poem might describe a busy city, or a beautiful landscape.*	
Narrative	The poem tells a story in a series of scenes or images.	*For example, a poem might show some key moments in a relationship.*	

a How is the poem 'Otherwise' on page 18 structured? Tick ✓ one of the structural methods above.

b On page 18, underline Ⓐ **all** the key words or phrases in the poem that create this structure.

c Write ✏ **one** or **two** sentences explaining in more detail how the poem is structured.

....

....

....

(2) The final lines of a poem are often the most significant: they reflect on and develop the ideas explored in the poem. Final lines can typically serve the following purposes:

A conclusion	Looking in a new light	A sudden reversal
The final lines connect, and reflect on, all the ideas in the poem.	The final lines look again at the key ideas in the poem in a very different way, leading the reader to think again about all that they have just read.	The final lines reflect on the key ideas in the poem and come to an unexpected or shocking realisation.

For example, having reflected on the things she does in her life, the writer of the poem 'Otherwise' could have:

concluded what a happy, peaceful life she has.	*revealed that her 'mate' has a very different view of their life together.*	*decided that happiness and peace are repetitive and boring – she wants excitement and change.*

a Which lines in the poem 'Otherwise' would you describe as its 'final lines'? Highlight ✏ them.

b How would you describe the final lines of the poem? Are they a **conclusion**, a **sudden reversal**, **looking in a new light**, or something else? Write ✏ **one** or **two** sentences explaining your ideas.

....

....

....

② How do I explore a poem's structural features?

Exploring key structural features, such as viewpoint, timeframe, repetition and contrast, can reveal some of the principal ways in which the poet presents ideas.

pronouns: used in place of a noun, e.g. 'I', 'you', 'he', 'she', 'it', 'we', 'they'

tense: a verb form indicating **when** an action took place, e.g. past tense, present tense

repetition: a word or phrase repeated for effect

contrast: two very different objects or ideas closely positioned to highlight their differences

① Looking at the poet's use of pronouns can reveal how the poet has used different **viewpoints** to structure the poem. Look at the poet's use of pronouns in 'Otherwise' on page 18. What does it reveal about the poem? Tick ✓ the viewpoint the writer has mainly used.

I	The poem is mainly focused on the thoughts and feelings of the speaker.	☐
you we	The poem focuses on the speaker's relationship with one or more other people.	☐
he she they	The poem is a reflection on characters whose actions, thoughts, etc. are described in the poem.	☐

② Looking at the poet's use of tense (e.g. the past tense, present tense, etc.) can reveal how the poet has structured the **timeframe** of the poem. In 'Otherwise', the poet writes about:

- the actual past: ....

- a possible past: ....

- a definite future: ....

Add 🖉 a quotation alongside each point to show where the poet has used these tenses.

③ **Repetition** can be used in a poem to highlight or emphasise a key idea.

  a Identify a word or phrase that is repeated in 'Otherwise' on page 18. Circle Ⓐ it every time it appears in the poem.

  b What idea is the poet emphasising through her repetition of this word or phrase? Write 🖉 **one** or **two** sentences explaining your ideas.

....

....

....

④ **Contrast** can be used in a poem to highlight a significant difference or change in two very different people, places or situations.

  a Identify an example of contrast in 'Otherwise' on page 18. Write 🖉 '**Contrast**' in the middle of the space to the right of the poem and draw 🖉 linking lines to all the ideas in the poem that highlight this contrast.

Look again at your answers to questions ② and ③.

  b What idea does this contrast highlight? Write 🖉 **one** or **two** sentences explaining your ideas.

....

....

....

③ How do I comment on structure?

Comments on the **effect** of the poet's use of **structure** can be used to develop your ideas, and help you to explore the poet's **intention**.

① Look at two **key ideas** from the poem that a student identified in their response to a question about the speaker's thoughts and feelings in the poem 'Otherwise'.

The speaker reflects on her happiness, and her good fortune in having that happiness. ☐	The speaker realises that her life will change. ☐

Which **one** of these key ideas do you agree with most strongly? Tick ✓ it.

② Now look at some of the **evidence** that the student selected to support their ideas.

'It might / have been otherwise.' ☐	'But one day, I know, / it will be otherwise.' ☐	The poet describes her day from when 'I got out of bed' until 'I slept in a bed'. ☐

Which evidence would you use to support the key idea you chose in question ①? Tick ✓ it.

③ Look at some **structural features** that the student focused on in exploring their ideas.

This sentence is repeated throughout the poem. ☐	The speaker contrasts the present with the future. ☐	The speaker uses the routine of her day to structure the poem. ☐

Which structural feature relates to your chosen key idea? Tick ✓ it.

④ The student also identified the **effect** of these structural features.

This highlights the elements of her life that bring her happiness. ☐	It emphasises her happiness and sense of relief that things have turned out as well as they have. ☐

This creates a strong sense of her fear that things must and will change. ☐

Which of these effects would you link to the structural feature you chose in question ③? Tick ✓ it.

⑤ The student reflected on what these structural features suggest about the poet's **intention**.

This suggests that the poem is a reflection on the inevitable change that happens as we grow old. ☐	This suggests that the poem is about the importance of knowing happiness cannot last. ☐

This suggests that the poem is about the importance of appreciating your life as it is at the moment, not in the future. ☐

Which **one** of these is most relevant to all the other ideas you have selected? Tick ✓ it.

Exploring structure

To explore the poet's structural choices effectively, you need to:

- identify how the poet has structured the poem: for example, over a period of time, through movement, using narrative, etc.
- identify some of the poem's key structural features: for example, the use of pronouns, tense, repetition, contrast, etc.
- consider the effect of structure and structural features, and their contribution to the poet's intention.

Look at this exam-style question you saw at the start of the unit.

Exam-style question

In 'Otherwise', how does the poet present the speaker's feelings about her life?   **(24 marks)**

Now look at a paragraph from one student's response to the question.

identifies a key idea in the poem

supports key idea with evidence

identifies a structural element or feature

> The speaker gives a strong impression that she thinks she is very fortunate in her life. The poem is structured around the events of a typical day in her life, for example, it begins when she 'got out of bed' and then 'ate cereal' and it ends as she 'slept in a bed'. Each of these events highlights a positive aspect of her life: for example, she has 'two strong legs', suggesting she is healthy and she has 'silver candlesticks', suggesting she has wealth. After each of these events, she repeats the phrase 'It might have been otherwise'. The poem's structure and the use of repetition strongly imply how grateful she feels that everything she does and has in her life makes her happy and comfortable and that she can choose how she spends and enjoys her days.

comments on the effect of the poet's structural choice

comments on how the effect of the structural choice supports the poet's intention

(1) Can you identify all the different things the student has included in this paragraph? Draw ✎ lines to link the annotations to the paragraph to show where the student has included them.

Your turn!

You are now going to **write two paragraphs** in response to the exam-style question.

Exam-style question

In 'Otherwise', how does the poet present the speaker's feelings about her life?   **(24 marks)**

(1) Which of the poem's **key ideas** will you focus on in your response? Note ✏ them below.

Paragraph 1	Paragraph 2

(2) Now think about some of the poet's **structural choices**. Which are relevant to the key ideas you have noted? Add ✏ them to your notes above.

(3) What **evidence** from the poem will you use to support your chosen key ideas and structural features? Add ✏ quotations to your notes above.

(4) What comments will you make on the **effect** of the poet's use of structure? What comments will you make on its **contribution to the poet's intention**? Add ✏ your ideas to your notes above.

(5) Review your notes. Tick ✓ the skills below you are ready to implement in the two paragraphs you are going to write.

☐ identify a key idea in the poem

☐ identify a structural feature that contributes to that key idea

☐ support your ideas with evidence from the poem

☐ explore the effect of the structural feature and its contribution to the poet's intention

(6) Now write ✏ **two** paragraphs on paper in response to the exam-style question above, exploring the poet's use of structure.

Review your skills

Check up

Review your response to the exam-style question on page 23. Tick ✓ the column to show how well you think you have done each of the following.

	Not quite ✓	Nearly there ✓	Got it! ✓
identified significant structural features	☐	☐	☐
explored the effect of structural features	☐	☐	☐
explored the contribution of structural features to the poet's intention	☐	☐	☐

Need more practice?

Here is another exam-style question, this time relating to 'Mother to Son' by Langston Hughes, which can be found on page 75.

Exam-style question

In 'Mother to Son', how does the poet present the speaker's feelings about her life?   **(24 marks)**

Write ✏ **two** paragraphs in response to the exam-style question, **focusing on the poet's structural choices**. You'll find some suggested points to refer to in the Answers section.

Comparison practice

Here is another exam-style question, relating to **both** 'Otherwise' by Jane Kenyon **and** 'Mother to Son' by Langston Hughes.

Exam-style question

In both 'Otherwise' and 'Mother to Son', the speakers think about the future. What are the similarities and/or differences between the ways the poets present the future?   **(8 marks)**

Write ✏ **one** or **two** paragraphs in response to the exam-style question, **comparing** the poet's use of structure in 'Otherwise' and 'Mother to Son'. You'll find some suggested points to refer to in the Answers section.

How confident do you feel about each of these **skills?** Colour ✏ in the bars.

1 How do I explore how a poem develops?

2 How do I explore a poem's structural features?

3 How do I comment on structure?

Analyse the language, form and structure used by a writer to create meanings and effects (AO2)

④ Exploring the poet's language choices

This unit will help you to explore the poet's language choices in an unseen poem. The skills you will build are to:

- identify significant language choices
- explore the effect of significant language choices
- comment on the poet's language choices.

In the exam you will face questions like the one below. This is about the poem on the next page. At the end of the unit you will **write two paragraphs** in response to this question.

Exam-style question

In 'City Lilacs', how does the speaker present her thoughts and feelings about the city?   **(24 marks)**

Before you tackle the question you will work through three key questions in the **skills boosts** to help you explore the poet's language choices.

① **How do I identify language choices that create a specific effect?**

② **How do I know what effect the poet is trying to create?**

③ **How do I comment on the poet's language choices?**

Read the poem on the next page. In Paper 2, Section C of your English Literature exam, you will write about one unseen poem, then compare it with another unseen poem.

As you read the poem, think about: ⊘

the impressions the poet creates of the city	the impressions the poet creates of the people who live and work in cities	the impressions the poet creates of lilacs.
☐	☐	☐

City Lilacs ✎

In crack-haunted alleys, overhangs,
plots of sour earth that pass for gardens,
in the space between wall and wheelie bin,

where men with mobiles make urgent conversation,
5   where bare-legged girls shiver in April winds,
where a new mother stands on her doorstep and blinks
at the brightness of morning, so suddenly born —

in all these places the city lilacs are pushing
their cones of blossom into the spring
10   to be taken by the warm wind.

Lilac, like love, makes no distinction.
It will open for anyone.
Even before love knows that it is love
lilac knows it must blossom.

15   In crack-haunted alleys, in overhangs,
in somebody's front garden
abandoned to crisp packets and cans,

on landscaped motorway roundabouts,
in the depth of parks
20   where men and women are lost in transactions
of flesh and cash, where mobiles ring

and the deal is done — here the city lilacs
release their sweet, wild perfume
then bow down, heavy with rain.

Helen Dunmore

① Write ✎ down **one** or **two** words or phrases to describe your impressions of the **three** different things the poet focuses on in the poem. As you note your ideas, label ✎ the line or phrase in the poem that creates each impression: **1a**, **1b**, etc.

The impression that the poet creates of...

1 the city	a
	b
2 people who live in the city	a
	b
3 the lilacs that grow in the city	a
	b

1 How do I identify language choices that create a specific effect?

When you read and write about a poem, aim to identify **rich, significant language choices** that the poet has chosen to create a specific effect on **you**, the reader.

To identify rich, significant language choices in the poem:

- focus on a small section of the poem at a time
- think about the poet's intention and your response to their ideas.

(1) Look at the **first** stanza of 'City Lilacs'.

Complete the sentences below by ticking ✓ **one** word or phrase that most accurately describes your response.

> In crack-haunted alleys, overhangs,
>
> plots of sour earth that pass for gardens,
>
> in the space between wall and wheelie bin,

a | *In this stanza, the poet describes*

the city ☐   the people in the city ☐   lilacs ☐

b | *The poet presents it/them as*

beautiful ☐   clean ☐   tame ☐   strong ☐   busy ☐

united ☐   warm ☐   happy ☐   ugly ☐   dirty ☐   wild ☐

weak ☐   quiet ☐   isolated ☐   cold ☐   miserable ☐

(2) Now think about each word in the first stanza above. Which words create the impressions you identified in question (1)?

a Cross out ~~cat~~ any words in the stanza that definitely do **not** create those impressions.

b Look at the words you have not crossed out. Which words create the impressions you have identified **most strongly**? Circle Ⓐ them.

(3) Now look at the **second** stanza of the poem.

> where men with mobiles make urgent conversation,
>
> where bare-legged girls shiver in April winds,
>
> where a new mother stands on her doorstep and blinks
>
> at the brightness of morning, so suddenly born —

a What is the poet describing? 🖉

....

b What impressions has the poet created of it/them? Note 🖉 them below. You could use some of the ideas above, or use your own.

....

....

c Which words or phrases in the stanza create these impressions most strongly? Circle Ⓐ them.

2 How do I know what effect the poet is trying to create?

> When you explore the effect of rich, significant language choices in a poem, or any text, think about the **connotations** of the word or phrase.

connotations: ideas or feelings that a word or phrase creates for the reader

1. Look at this phrase in the **first** stanza of 'City Lilacs' on page 26.

> In crack-haunted alleys, overhangs,
> plots of sour earth that pass for gardens,
> in the space between wall and wheelie bin,

Think about the connotations of the word 'sour' in this stanza.

Which ideas does it create in your mind?

Tick ✓ any of the ideas on the right, and/or

add 🖉 your own.

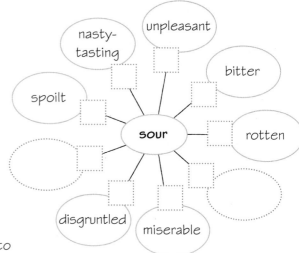

nasty-tasting   unpleasant   bitter   spoilt   sour   rotten   disgruntled   miserable

2. The poet could have chosen different adjectives to describe the plots of earth in the city. What connotations would the following language choices have created? Note 🖉 **two** ideas alongside each alternative word.

rich ....

sweet ....

plots of **sour** earth

poor ....

starved ....

3. Review your answers above. Write 🖉 **one** or **two** sentences summing up your ideas about the poet's choice of the word 'sour' to describe the 'earth' in this city.

....

....

....

4. Now look at these lines from the **second** stanza of 'City Lilacs'.

> where men with mobiles make urgent conversation,
>
> where bare-legged girls shiver in April winds,

Circle Ⓐ **one** significant language choice in this stanza. Annotate 🖉 it, identifying the connotations of your chosen word.

③ How do I comment on the poet's language choices?

The most effective comments on the poet's language choices focus on their **effect** on the reader and how they support the poet's **intention**.

> intention: the impact the writer intends the text to have on the reader

① Look at this opening sentence of one student's analysis of 'City Lilacs' on page 26.

> In the first line of the poem, the poet begins her description of the city with the image of 'crack-haunted alleys'.

This student could add one or more of the following comments to their sentence above.

A The poet is saying that the tarmac in the alleys is full of cracks. ☐

B This immediately gives the impression of a rundown and neglected city. ☐

C The word 'crack' could suggest neglect or it could suggest a drug problem haunts the city. ☐

D The word 'haunted' suggests this is an unwelcoming and frightening place. ☐

E This is a good description because you can imagine it in your mind. ☐

  a Some of the comments above are **ineffective** because:
- they do not make a comment and are too vague. Label ✏ them '**vague**' and cross ✕ them.
- they do not make a comment; they just describe what the writer has done. Label ✏ them '**describe**' and cross ✕ them.

  b Some of the comments above are **effective** because:
- they comment on the effect of a poetic device. Label ✏ them '**effect**' and tick ✓ them.
- they comment on how the device supports the poet's intention. Label ✏ them '**intention**' and tick ✓ them.

② The student's next paragraph begins: | The poet then describes 'plots of sour earth'.

The student could add one or more of these comments. EITHER cross ✕ and label ✏ them '**vague**' or '**describe**' OR tick ✓ and label ✏ them '**effect**' or '**intention**'.

A The word 'sour' implies that the earth is rotten, perhaps suggesting pollution. ☐

B I think this is describing the gardens of the houses in the city. ☐

C The poet creates the impression of a ruined and polluted city where nothing will grow. ☐

D The word 'sour' makes me think this is not a good place. ☐

E This helps to convey the feeling of a place that no one cares about or looks after. ☐

Exploring the poet's language choices

To comment effectively on the poet's language choices, you need to:

- identify rich, significant language choices that contribute to the impressions created in the poem
- explore the connotations of the poet's language choices
- comment on their effect and their contribution to the poet's intention.

Now look at this exam-style question you saw at the start of the unit.

Exam-style question

In 'City Lilacs', how does the speaker present her thoughts and feelings about the city? **(24 marks)**

Now look at a paragraph from one student's response to the question.

identifies a key idea in the poem

identifies a significant language choice

The poet then contrasts her description of a broken and neglected city with her description of the lilacs that grow there. She describes the lilacs 'pushing' their way into the city, which suggests their strength and power as though it takes a massive effort to squeeze into this crowded and unwelcoming place, and giving the impression of nature as powerful and something that will always survive. This strength of nature makes the city seem a better place, as though there is life and strength, not just loneliness and decay.

comments on the connotations/ effect of language choice

comments on how language choice supports the poet's intention

(1) Can you identify all the different things the student has included in this paragraph? Draw 🖉 lines to link the annotations to the paragraph to show where the student has included them.

Your turn!

You are now going to **write two paragraphs** in response to the exam-style question.

Exam-style question

In 'City Lilacs', how does the speaker present her thoughts and feelings about the city?   **(24 marks)**

(1) Re-read the poem on page 26. Review your first impressions, which you noted on the same page. Are these still the impressions the poem creates? Adjust 🖉 your answers on page 26 if you need to.

(2) Now choose **two** sections of the poem to focus on in your response. Choose sections which create a strong impression of the city. Label 🖉 them **1** and **2**.

(3) Look at the two sections of the poem you have selected. Circle Ⓐ any rich, significant vocabulary choices in these sections that help to create a strong impression of the city.

(4) In the planning space below, note 🖉 down impressions created in the two sections of the poem you have selected.

1	2

(5) Add 🖉 relevant quotations featuring significant vocabulary choices to your notes above.

(6) Annotate 🖉 significant vocabulary choices in each of your quotations with ideas about their connotations: what ideas and feelings do the poet's language choices create?

(7) Write 🖉 **two** paragraphs on paper in response to the exam-style question above, focusing on the poet's language choices.

Review your skills

Check up

Review your response to the exam-style question on page 31. Tick ⊘ the column to show how well you think you have done each of the following.

	Not quite ⊘	Nearly there ⊘	Got it! ⊘
identified significant language choices	☐	☐	☐
commented on their effect	☐	☐	☐
commented on their contribution to the poet's intention	☐	☐	☐

Need more practice?

Here is another exam-style question, this time relating to 'A Letter in October' by Ted Kooser, which can be found on page 76.

Exam-style question

In 'A Letter in October', how does the speaker present his thoughts and feelings about the place where he lives?   (24 marks)

Write ✐ **two** paragraphs in response to the exam-style question, **focusing on the poet's language choices**. You'll find some suggested points to refer to in the Answers section.

Comparison practice

Here is another exam-style question, relating to **both** 'City Lilacs' by Helen Dunmore **and** 'A Letter in October' by Ted Kooser.

Exam-style question

In both 'City Lilacs' and 'A Letter in October', the speakers describe features of the natural world. What are the similarities and/or differences between the ways the poets present nature?   (8 marks)

Write ✐ **one** or **two** paragraphs in response to the exam-style question, **comparing** the poet's language choices in 'City Lilacs' and 'A Letter in October'.

How confident do you feel about each of these **skills?** Colour ✐ in the bars.

1 How do I identify language choices that create a specific effect?

2 How do I know what effect the poet is trying to create?

3 How do I comment on the poet's language choices?

Analyse the language, form and structure used by a writer to create meanings and effects (AO2)

⑤ Exploring poetic devices

This unit will help you to explore some of the language devices poets use to create meaning and effects. The skills you will build are to:

- identify and explore the impact of sound devices in a poem
- identify and explore the impact of imagery in a poem
- comment effectively on the poet's use of language devices.

In the exam you will face questions like the one below. This is about the poem on the next page. At the end of the unit you will **write two paragraphs** in response to this question.

Exam-style question

In 'The Round', how does the speaker present his thoughts and feelings about the day on which he wrote this poem?

(24 marks)

Before you tackle the question you will work through three key questions in the **skills boosts** to help you explore the poet's use of poetic devices.

 ① How do I explore sound devices in a poem?   **② How do I explore the imagery in a poem?**   **③ How do I comment on the poet's use of poetic devices?**

Read the poem on the next page. In Paper 2, Section C of your English Literature exam, you will write about one unseen poem, then compare it with another unseen poem.

As you read the poem, think about: ✓

where the speaker is in the first part of the poem	why the speaker goes inside in the second part of the poem	the thoughts and feelings the poet expresses in the final part of the poem.
☐	☐	☐

The Round 🖉

Light splashed this morning
on the shell-pink **anemones**
swaying on their tall stems;
down blue-spiked **veronica**
5   light flowed in rivulets
over the humps of the honeybees;
this morning I saw light kiss
the silk of the roses
in their second flowering,
10   my late bloomers
flushed with their brandy.
A curious gladness shook me.

So I have shut the doors of my house,
so I have trudged downstairs to my cell,
15   so I am sitting in semi-dark
hunched over my desk
with nothing for a view
to tempt me
but a bloated compost heap,
20   steamy old stinkpile,
under my window;
and I pick my notebook up
and I start to read aloud
the still-wet words I scribbled
25   on the blotted page:
"Light splashed . . ."

I can scarcely wait till tomorrow
when a new life begins for me,
as it does each day,
30   as it does each day.

Stanley Kunitz

anemones, veronica: flowering plants often found in a garden

1 **a** Which of the dictionary definitions below might the poet have intended? Tick ✓ **one** or **more**.

> **round** (noun)
>
> **a** a circular slice of something: *two rounds of toast.*   ☐
>
> **b** visits made to a number of people or places in turn:
>   *I have a newspaper round, delivering papers in my local area.*   ☐
>
> **c** one of a series of sessions or stages: *United are in the third round of the Cup.*   ☐
>
> **d** a regularly repeated sequence of activities:
>   *My life is a daily round of school, homework and sleep.*   ☐

b Write 🖉 **one** sentence explaining why you think this definition is most relevant.

....

Sound devices are language techniques that use the sound of a word or phrase to add to its impact.

onomatopoeia	a word whose sound imitates its meaning	bang crash
alliteration	words beginning with, or containing, the same letter or sound, positioned close to each other	fee<u>l</u>ings of <u>l</u>ove <u>l</u>inger
assonance	words with similar vowel sounds, placed close to each other	b<u>a</u>d h<u>a</u>bits c<u>a</u>n tr<u>a</u>vel

(1) Circle Ⓐ and label 🖉 examples of 'onomatopoeia', 'alliteration', or 'assonance' in the extracts below from 'The Round' on page 34.

> A   Light splashed this morning
>
> on the shell-pink anemones
>
> swaying on their tall stems;

> B   light flowed in rivulets
>
> over the humps of the honeybees;

(2) Read aloud any words you labelled 'onomatopoeia'. Why do you think the writer chose to use this device? Tick ✓ **one** or **more** of the ideas below, or add 🖉 your own.

It sounds good.	☐	It adds emphasis to the idea.	☐	....

It makes the description more vivid.	☐	You can hear <u>and</u> see what the poet is describing.	☐

(3) a Look at the words you labelled 'alliteration' in question **(1)**. Highlight 🖉 the alliterative letters. Read the lines aloud, emphasising the sound of the highlighted letters. Ask yourself:

- are they letters with **hard sounds** (e.g. 'k', 'p') or **soft sounds** (e.g. 's', 'w')?
- how does the sound of the letters contribute to the mood or impression of the poem?

b Complete 🖉 one student's comments on the effect of this alliteration in the lines in question, using the ideas below.

> The hard alliterative sounds in these lines create a .... *mood*
>
> ....
>
> The soft alliterative sounds in these lines create a .... *mood*
>
> ....

| peaceful, quiet | suggesting the sound of | machinery | splashing water |
| violent, aggressive | creating an impression of | a gentle breeze | breaking glass |

(4) Assonance and alliteration can both create a strong link between words. Look at any phrases you labelled 'assonance' or 'alliteration' in question **(1)**. Tick ✓ **one** or **more** of the ideas below to show their effect, or add 🖉 your own.

It sounds good.	☐	It adds emphasis to the idea.	☐	....

It links two words to highlight a surprising image.	☐	It makes the description more vivid.	☐

2 How do I explore the imagery in a poem?

Imagery is the use of words to create visual images in the reader's mind. Writers often achieve this using **figurative language** techniques: simile, metaphor and personification.

simile	a comparison made using 'like' or 'as'
metaphor	a direct comparison
personification	a kind of metaphor that gives human actions or qualities to non-human objects

Similes are easy to identify:

- look for 'like' or 'as'
- is the writer comparing two things?

Metaphors are harder to spot:

- look for unusual or surprising word choices
- is the writer effectively comparing two things?

For example:

> Light splashed this morning ——— *surprising word choice?*
>
> on the (shell-pink) anemones ——— *comparing colour of a flower to colour of a shell?*

(1) In the lines above from 'The Round' on page 34, has the writer used any other similes or metaphors? Circle Ⓐ and label 🖉 them.

(2) Look at this metaphor from the poem.

> down blue-spiked veronica ———*compares movement of light to movement of water*
>
> (light flowed) in rivulets

Why do you think the poet has chosen to compare light and water in this metaphor? Think about the **qualities** and **connotations** of water.

| clean | pure | life-giving | refreshing | wet | fluid | sparkle | soak | pour |

Write 🖉 **one** or **two** sentences explaining your ideas. You could use some of the ideas above.

....

....

....

(3) Personification can also be a tricky technique to spot; look for surprising verb choices describing actions that are usually done only by humans. Look at the extract on the right.

> this morning I saw light (kiss)
>
> the silk of the roses

a Annotate 🖉 the word 'kiss' with any qualities or connotations the word suggests to you.

b Why do you think the poet chose to describe the light landing on some roses as a 'kiss'? Write 🖉 **one** or **two** sentences explaining your ideas.

....

....

....

③ How do I comment on the poet's use of poetic devices?

The most effective comments on language and language devices focus on their **effect** on the reader and how they support the poet's **intention**.

① Look at these opening sentences of one student's analysis of 'The Round' on page 34.

> In the first part of the poem, the poet describes the beauty of his garden using surprising and vivid imagery. He describes seeing how the 'light splashed' on the flowers.

This student could add one or more of the following comments to their sentences above.

A This metaphor says that the light is like water. ☐

B This metaphor makes the movement of the light seem more dynamic and dramatic. ☐

C This metaphor makes the reader think. ☐

D This metaphor helps you imagine what it looked like more clearly. ☐

E This metaphor shows the poet's wonder and excitement at the beauty of the natural world. ☐

a Some of the comments above are **ineffective** because:
  • they do not make a comment and are too vague. Label 🖉 them '**vague**' and cross ⊗ them.
  • they do not make a comment; they just describe what the writer has done. Label 🖉 them '**describe**' and cross ⊗ them.

b Some of the comments above are **effective** because:
  • they comment on the effect of a poetic device. Label 🖉 them '**effect**' and tick ✓ them.
  • they comment on how the device supports the poet's intention. Label 🖉 them '**intention**' and tick ✓ them.

② The student's next paragraph begins:

> The poet uses alliteration in his description: 'splashed', 'swaying... stems'...

The student could add one or more of these comments. EITHER cross ⊗ and label 🖉 them '**vague**' or '**describe**' OR tick ✓ and label 🖉 them '**effect**' or '**intention**'.

A This alliteration uses lots of words beginning with 's'. ☐

B This alliteration sounds very effective and interesting. ☐

C This alliteration suggests the sound of a gentle breeze blowing through the flowers. ☐

D This alliteration creates a vivid impression of both the sight and sound of the poet's garden. ☐

E This alliteration suggests the calm, peaceful quiet of early morning. ☐

Exploring poetic devices

To explore poetic devices effectively, you need to:

- identify any sound devices the poet has used
- identify any imagery the poet has used
- comment on their effect and their contribution to the poet's intention.

Look at this exam-style question you saw at the start of the unit.

Exam-style question

In 'The Round', how does the speaker present his thoughts and feelings about the day on which he wrote this poem?

(24 marks)

Now look at a paragraph from one student's response to the question.

identifies a key idea in the poem

identifies a poetic device

> In the second part of the poem, the speaker goes into his house to finish a poem about his experience in the garden. He uses the verb 'trudged' to suggest how reluctant he is to leave the beauty of the outside world, and describes the place he goes to write the poem in very negative terms. He uses the metaphor of a 'cell' to describe it, suggesting it is small and like being in prison. He describes his view of a compost heap as a 'steamy old stinkpile'. The alliteration of the letter 's' in this description almost suggests the hiss of the stinking fumes wafting up from the compost heap and floating in through his window. Both of these images use poetic devices to emphasise the difference between his experience inside the house, writing about the beauty of nature, compared with his experience outside the house, actually enjoying the beauty of nature.

comments on the effect of a poetic device

comments on how poetic devices support the poet's intention

① Can you identify all the different things the student has included in this paragraph? Draw ✐ lines to link the annotations to the paragraph to show where the student has included them.

Your turn!

You are now going to **write two paragraphs** in response to the exam-style question, focusing on the poet's use of **poetic devices**.

Exam-style question

In 'The Round', how does the speaker present his thoughts and feelings about the day on which he wrote this poem?   **(24 marks)**

(1) Look again at 'The Round' on page 34. Tick ✓ **all** the poetic devices the poet uses.

Sound devices
alliteration
onomatopoeia
assonance

Imagery
simile
metaphor
personification

(2) Look for key ideas where the poet uses a poetic device to add to their effect and impact.

a   Note ✏ down **two** key ideas in the poem that you will focus on in your response to the question.

b   Add ✏ quotations to your plan, labelling the poetic device the poet has used in each one.

(3) What is the effect of the poetic devices in the quotations you have noted? Add ✏ to your notes.

(4) What is the poet's intention in the ideas and quotations you have noted? Add ✏ to your notes.

(5) Now write ✏ **two** paragraphs on paper in response to the above exam-style question, focusing on the poet's use of poetic devices.

Remember: Don't simply list poetic devices that the poet uses. Only comment on poetic devices where they make a significant contribution to the poem's effect and the poet's intention.

Review your skills

Check up

Review your response to the exam-style question on page 39. Tick ⊘ the column to show how well you think you have done each of the following.

	Not quite ⊘	Nearly there ⊘	Got it! ⊘
explored the poet's use of sound devices	☐	☐	☐
explored the poet's use of imagery	☐	☐	☐
commented on poetic devices' effect and contribution to the poet's intention	☐	☐	☐

Need more practice?

Here is another exam-style question, this time relating to 'A Letter in October' by Ted Kooser, which can be found on page 76.

Exam-style question

In 'A Letter in October', how does the speaker present his thoughts and feelings about October?

(24 marks)

Write ✏ **two** paragraphs in response to the exam-style question, **focusing on the poet's use of poetic devices**. You'll find some suggested points to refer to in the Answers section.

Comparison practice

Here is another exam-style question relating to **both** 'The Round' by Stanley Kunitz **and** 'A Letter in October' by Ted Kooser.

Exam-style question

In both 'The Round' and 'A Letter in October', the speakers describe the natural world. What are the similarities and/or differences between the ways the poets present nature? (8 marks)

Write ✏ **one** or **two** paragraphs in response to the exam-style question, **comparing** the poet's use of poetic devices in 'The Round' and 'A Letter in October'.

How confident do you feel about each of these **skills?** Colour ✏ in the bars.

1 How do I explore sound devices in a poem?

2 How do I explore the imagery in a poem?

3 How do I comment on the poet's use of poetic devices?

Analyse the language, form and structure used by a writer to create meanings and effects (AO2)

⑥ Exploring the poet's use of form

This unit will help you to understand and explore how a poet uses form to create meaning and effects. The skills you will build are to:

* explore the form of a poem
* explore rhyme and rhythm in a poem
* comment effectively on the form of a poem.

In the exam you will face questions like the one below. This is about the poem on the next page. At the end of the unit you will **write two paragraphs** in response to this question.

Exam-style question

In 'Postcard', how does the speaker present the end of summer? **(24 marks)**

Before you tackle the question you will work through three key questions in the **skills boosts** to help you explore the form of a poem.

 How do I explore form?

 How do I explore rhythm and rhyme?

 How do I comment on the poet's use of form?

Read the poem on the next page. In Paper 2, Section C of your English Literature exam, you will write about one unseen poem, then compare it with another unseen poem.

As you read the poem, think about:

the shape of the poem on the page. Is it neat and regular, or unpredictable and irregular?	any patterns or repetitions the poet has used to organise her ideas	how these patterns change or develop in the poem.

Postcard ✎

I saw a muskrat nose across a pond
nudging the reeds apart without a sound.

I saw a spider touched by a note of sun
shake out its net, bouncing it up and down.

5   I saw a black snake slipping off the road;
in the doorway, pulsing, a tiny golden toad.

I saw a white owl, baffled by the light
bank silently and sheer off out of sight.

These things took place the day the summer went.
10 I noted them down, not knowing what they meant

or if anything at all had really happened.
Only a state of mind in which eyes, opened

by solitude, could see the lives that other
creatures made, busy and unperturbed by love

15 or hate. I pull the shutters inward, drop the bar
but wind and dark still forage at my door.

Beatrice Garland

(1) When did the poet write this poem, do you think?
Underline (A) **two** clues you are given in the poem.

How is the weather described
at the end of the poem?

(2) Which stanzas tell you most about the things the speaker sees? Label ✎ them '**what she sees**'.

(3) Which stanzas tell you most about the speaker's reaction to the things she sees? Label ✎ them
'**reaction**'.

(4) **a** How would you describe the form of this poem? Tick ✓ **all** the features below that you can
identify.

A   Lines are a regular length.   ☐

        B   Lines are an irregular length.   ☐

C   Stanzas have the same number of lines.   ☐

        D   Stanzas have a different number of lines.   ☐

E   Uses rhyme and half-rhyme.   ☐

        F   Does not use any rhyme.   ☐

G   Uses repetition.   ☐

        H   Does not use repetition.   ☐

b Highlight ✎ examples of each feature in the poem and label them **A, B, C,** etc.

How do I explore form?

Before you can comment on form, you need to identify some of the features of form that the poet has used, then consider their effect.

One of the most immediately obvious features of a poem is the poet's choice of form. Look at the poem on the page and ask yourself: is the poem written in a **regular form**, with each stanza following a similar pattern? Or is it written in **free verse** with no obvious pattern?

Look at 'Postcard' on page 42. The writer chose a **regular form** but she could have expressed the same ideas in **free verse**.

> I saw a muskrat nose
> across a pond nudging the reeds apart
> without a sound.
>
> I saw a spider
>
> touched by a note
> of sun shake out its net, bouncing it
> up and
> down.

> I saw a muskrat nose across a pond
> nudging the reeds apart without a sound.
>
> I saw a spider touched by a note of sun
> shake out its net, bouncing it up and down.

(1) Compare the two different versions of these stanzas. Which forms create which effects most powerfully? Complete the table below, ticking ✓ **regular form**, **free verse**, **both** or **neither**.

		Regular form ✓	Free verse ✓	Neither ✓
A	suggests a series of scenes or snapshots	☐	☐	☐
B	creates a gentle, reflective mood	☐	☐	☐
C	creates a mood of excitement or amazement	☐	☐	☐
D	imitates the informal patterns of everyday speech	☐	☐	☐
E	suggests a surprising sequence of random images	☐	☐	☐
F	highlights key words/phrases in each description	☐	☐	☐

(2) Now think about some of the other features of form you might find in a poem. For example:
- any repetition of words or phrases in the poem
- a sudden change in the form or pattern of stanzas.

(a) Can you identify either of these features in the poem on page 42? Highlight and label ✎ them '**repetition**' or '**change in form/pattern**'.

(b) What effect do the features you identified have? On paper, write ✎ **one** or **two** sentences describing the effects of the features you identified. You could use some of the ideas in question (1) to help you.

How do I explore rhythm and rhyme?

How do you talk when you are thinking aloud? How do you talk when you are angry, or happy, or miserable, or excited? Poets use rhythm to reflect those speech patterns and create the mood, pace and emphasis they want to achieve.

mood: the feeling or emotion created in a text
pace: the speed at which the ideas in a text develop or are expressed
emphasis: a specific word or phrase is highlighted or given more importance

Rhyme and rhythm work together to create **mood**, **pace** and **emphasis**.

① Compare the three versions of the **first** stanza of the poem 'Postcard' below. Try reading them aloud to hear the impact of rhyme and rhythm.

1. The original version:

I saw a muskrat nose across a pond
nudging the reeds apart without a sound.

2. ...now without the rhyme:

I saw a muskrat nose across a lake
nudging the reeds apart without a noise.

3. ...now with a different rhythm:

I saw a muskrat that was nosing silently across a lake nudging its way through the reeds

a What impact do the rhyme and rhythm of the original have? Complete the sentences below by circling Ⓐ any words to the right.

Remember: The changes may affect more than one aspect of the poem.

• Taking out the **rhyme** changes the:	mood	pace	emphasis
• Changing the **rhythm** changes the:	mood	pace	emphasis

b Write ✏ **one** or **two** sentences, describing the mood, pace, or emphasis created by rhyme and rhythm in the original version.

....

....

....

End-stopped lines can emphasise the rhythm of a poem. The use of **enjambment** can change the mood and/or pace of the poem and allow specific phrases to be emphasised.

end-stopped: when a line of poetry ends with a punctuation mark
enjambment: when a sentence runs on without pause from one line or stanza to the next.

② Look closely at the last **four** stanzas of 'Postcard' on page 42. Read them aloud. Cross out ~~cat~~ any unnecessary words in the sentences below so they accurately describe the effects of enjambment in these lines.

The use of enjambment in the last four stanzas:
• <u>maintains / changes</u> the **pace** of the poem, making it <u>faster / slower</u>.
• <u>maintains / changes</u> the **mood** of the poem, making it <u>more / less</u> <u>anxious / excited / angry / reflective</u>.
• gives **emphasis** to the <u>word / phrase</u> <u>'busy' / 'unperturbed by love' / 'or hate' / 'wind and dark'</u>.

③ How do I comment on the poet's use of form?

The most effective comments on the poet's use of form focus on the **effect** of the poet's choices on the reader and how they support the poet's **intention**.

intention: the impact that the writer intends the text to have on the reader

① Re-read the poem 'Postcard' on page 42. Draw lines to link some of the boxes below to summarise your comments on the form of the poem.

In the first part of the poem

In the second part of the poem

the poet uses a regular stanza form

the poet uses a regular rhythm and rhyme

the poet uses free verse

the poet uses enjambment

to create a series of scenes or snapshots

to focus on different ideas or aspects of a scene or idea

to suggest disconnected or random thoughts

to suggest the patterns of everyday speech

to create a slower, measured pace

to create a regular, even pace

to create a faster pace

to create a reflective, thoughtful mood

to create a mood of excitement

to suggest that the speaker's thoughts are suddenly racing

to create an anxious, unsettled mood

Learn the spelling of **rhythm**. The first three letters are the same as 'rhyme' – and it has two 'h's, one 'y' and **no vowels**. Think: <u>r</u>hythm <u>h</u>elps <u>y</u>our <u>t</u>wo <u>h</u>ips <u>m</u>ove.

② Which of the features of form below would you expect to find in (and use if you were writing):
- an angry poem about the end of a relationship? Label them **A** for 'angry'.
- a poem exploring happy memories? Label them **M** for 'memories'.
- a poem about childhood? Label them **C** for 'childhood'.

a regular stanza form ⬚   free verse ⬚

a regular rhythm ⬚   no regular rhythm ⬚   enjambment ⬚

short lines ⬚   longer lines ⬚

some rhyme and half rhyme ⬚   no rhyme ⬚

a slower pace ⬚   a regular, even pace ⬚   a faster pace ⬚

Exploring the poet's use of form

To comment effectively on the poet's use of form, you need to:
- identify features of the poem's form that have a significant effect
- explore their effect on the reader and/or contribution to the poet's intention.

Now look again at the exam-style question you saw at the start of the unit.

Exam-style question

In 'Postcard', how does the speaker present the end of summer? **(24 marks)**

Look at these paragraphs taken from students' responses to the question.

Student A

The poem is written in stanzas of two lines. These are called couplets. The poet uses rhyme and half rhyme to link each pair of lines, for example, 'pond' and 'sound', and there is quite a regular rhythm which helps the poem flow. The poet also uses enjambment which means that some lines flow into the next one without stopping. This is quite effective.

Student B

In the second part of the poem the poet uses enjambment to hurry the pace of the poem, suggesting fast-moving thoughts as the speaker reflects on the idea that animals' lives are 'busy and unperturbed by love / or hate'. Finishing this sentence so quickly on the new line brings the hurried pace to a sudden halt, which emphasises the phrase 'or hate' and suggests that the speaker, unlike the animals, _is_ feeling perturbed and is especially perturbed by hate.

Student C

The poet uses each one of the first four stanzas of the poem to show snapshots from the speaker's life on the last day of summer. Each stanza follows a similar pattern, using a similar rhythm, and repetition of the phrase 'I saw', to create an even, measured pace suggesting a calm mood of reflection. It creates the impression of a quiet walk through the countryside, observing wildlife as the summer comes to an end.

	Student A ✓	Student B ✓	Student C ✓	None ✓
① a Which students have identified significant features of the poem's form?	☐	☐	☐	☐
b Which students have commented effectively on the **effect** of the poem's form or the poet's **intention**?	☐	☐	☐	☐

Your turn!

You are now going to **write two paragraphs** in response to the exam-style question, focusing on the poet's **use of form**.

Exam-style question

In 'Postcard', how does the speaker present the end of summer?   (24 marks)

In your response, you could focus on some of these key ideas in the poem:

- the animals described ——————— I saw a spider touched by a note of sun

- feelings of love and hate —————— the lives that other
creatures made, busy and unperturbed by love
or hate. I pull the shutters inward, drop the bar
- the arrival of autumn ——————— but wind and dark still forage at my door.

(1) Use the planning space below to note 🖊 **two** key ideas in the poem on which you will focus in your response. You could use some of the ideas above, and/or your own ideas.

(2) How does the poet's use of form contribute to these ideas? Add 🖊 quotations and notes to the planning space above.

(3) Review your notes. Have you focused on the **effect** of the poet's use of form? Adjust 🖊 your notes as necessary.

(4) Write 🖊 **two** paragraphs on paper in response to the exam-style question above, focusing on the poet's use of form.

Review your skills

Check up

Review your response to the exam-style question on page 47. Tick ✓ the column to show how well you think you have done each of the following.

	Not quite ✓	Nearly there ✓	Got it! ✓
identified significant features of form	☐	☐	☐
commented on their effect and/or contribution to the poet's intention	☐	☐	☐

Need more practice?

Here is another exam-style question, this time relating to 'A Letter in October' by Ted Kooser, which can be found on page 76.

Exam-style question

In 'A Letter in October', how does the speaker present his thoughts and feelings about October?
(24 marks)

Write 🖉 **two** paragraphs in response to the exam-style question, **focusing on the poet's use of form**. You'll find some suggested points to refer to in the Answers section.

Comparison practice

Here is another exam-style question, relating to **both** 'Postcard' by Beatrice Garland **and** 'A Letter in October' by Ted Kooser.

Exam-style question

In both 'Postcard' and 'A Letter in October', the speakers describe the natural world. What are the similarities and/or differences between the ways the poets present nature?
(8 marks)

Write 🖉 **one** or **two** paragraphs in response to the exam-style question, **comparing** the poets' use of form in 'Postcard' and 'A Letter in October'.

How confident do you feel about each of these **skills?** Colour 🖉 in the bars.

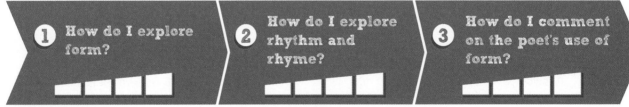

1 How do I explore form?

2 How do I explore rhythm and rhyme?

3 How do I comment on the poet's use of form?

Read, understand and respond to texts (AO1); Analyse the language, form and structure used by a writer to create meanings and effects (AO2)

(7) Writing about one poem

This unit will help you to write your response to the first part of the question on unseen poetry in your exam: writing about one poem. The skills you will build are to:

- annotate a poem
- explore how different elements of a poem work together to create effects
- select and sequence significant points to make in your response.

In the exam you will face a question like the one below. This is about the poem on the next page. At the end of the unit you will **plan and write your response** to this question.

Exam-style question

In 'Strawberries', how does the speaker present his thoughts and feelings?   **(24 marks)**

Before you tackle the question you will work through three key questions in the **skills boosts** to help you plan your response and write effectively about the poem.

 1 How do I annotate a poem?

2 How do the elements of a poem work together?

 3 How do I structure my response?

Read the poem on the next page. In Paper 2, Section C of your English Literature exam, you will write about one unseen poem, then compare it with another unseen poem.

As you read the poem, think about:

| who and/or what the poem is about | how you would summarise the poem and your response to it | any of the poet's choices that make a significant impression on you. |

Strawberries

There were never strawberries
like the ones we had
that sultry afternoon
sitting on the step
5   of the open french window
facing each other
your knees held in mine
the blue plates in our laps
the strawberries glistening
10   in the hot sunlight
we dipped them in sugar
looking at each other
not hurrying the feast
for one to come
15   the empty plates
laid on the stone together
with the two forks crossed
and I bent towards you
sweet in that air
20   in my arms
abandoned like a child
from your eager mouth
the taste of strawberries
in my memory
25   lean back again
let me love you

let the sun beat
on our forgetfulness
one hour of all
30   the heat intense
and summer lightning
on the **Kilpatrick hills**

let the storm wash the plates

Edwin Morgan

Kilpatrick hills: an area in Scotland

(1) Which word, phrase or line in the poem do you find particularly effective? Underline (A) it, then write (✎) **one** or **two** sentences explaining your choice.

....

....

....

....

....

....

How do I annotate a poem?

Don't start with a checklist of features to spot in the poem – similes, metaphors, rhyme, enjambment, etc. Start with the poem and your response to the ideas you find in it. You can then think about how the poet's choices have shaped those ideas and your response.

① When you first read a poem, aim only to understand what it is about. Then read it again to make sure you feel confident in your understanding. Write ✏ **one** short sentence summarising the poem 'Strawberries' on page 50.

....

....

② Read the poem a third time. Identify any words, phrases or ideas that seem significant in shaping your understanding. For example:

a When did you first realise that the poem is about two lovers? Underline Ⓐ the word or phrase in the poem on page 50 that first suggested this idea to you.

b Annotate ✏ the rest of the poem, noting what happens, and your impressions of the people, or events, keeping your notes on the **left-hand side of the poem.** Save the space on the right-hand side for annotating some of the poet's choices.

> For more on understanding and responding to a poem, see Units 1 and 2.

③ Are there any words, phrases, ideas or images that surprised or mystified you in this poem? Circle Ⓐ them. Think about why the poet might have used them. These are the parts of the poem that might create the most effective and interesting response. For example:

a Why might the poet have chosen strawberries as the food the lovers eat in the poem? Why not an apple, or cake, or crisps? Annotate ✏ the title of the poem with your ideas.

b Look at lines 15–17 of the poem. Why might the poet have chosen to use this image?

> the empty plates
> laid on the stone together
> with the two forks crossed

Annotate these lines in the poem with your ideas, then note them on the **right-hand side of the poem.** ✏

c Now annotate ✏ any other words or phrases that seem significant in creating the ideas and impressions you have already noted on the poem. Think about what they suggest, their connotations, and how they shape your ideas and impressions.

> For more on language and poetic devices, see Units 4 and 5.

④ You can now begin to think about the poet's choices of form and structure. For example:

a The poem is written in very short lines. What effect does this have on your impressions, and the mood or pace of the poem? Note ✏ your ideas on the **right-hand side of the poem.**

b The final line of the poem is given its own stanza. What effect does this have? Annotate ✏ the final line with your ideas, noting them on the **right-hand side of the poem**.

c Can you identify any other significant features of form and/or structure? How do they contribute to the mood or pace of the poem? Annotate ✏ the poem with your ideas, noting them on the **right-hand side of the poem.**

> For more on structure and form, see Units 3 and 6.

Skills boost

2 How do the elements of a poem work together?

Aim to fully explore each piece of evidence you select, thinking about how different choices of language and/or form and structure work together.

1. Think about all the different language choices in a quotation. Look at one student's annotations below of **two different language choices** in lines 20–21 of 'Strawberries' on page 50. The speaker describes his lover being:

two meanings:
1. uninhibited, carefree, unrestrained
2. deserted, left alone

in my arms
(abandoned) (like a child) ——— *helpless, innocent, vulnerable?*

together these suggest lover's been deserted, left in his arms, like a helpless child?
Or that lover is carefree and innocent like a child?
Or both?

Write ✏ **one** or **two** sentences, commenting on the poet's language choices in these lines. You could use the notes above to help you, or your own ideas.

....

....

....

....

....

2. Think about how language and structure work together in a quotation. Look at one student's annotations below of **a language choice and a structure choice** in lines 27–28 of the poem.

short, simple language choices

let the sun (beat) ——— *suggests strength, violence?*
on our forgetfulness ——— *last word on short line – adds emphasis*

Write ✏ **one** or **two** sentences commenting on the poet's choices of language and structure in these lines. You could use the notes above to help you, or your own ideas.

....

....

....

....

....

3 How do I structure my response?

There are a number of ways in which you can organise a response to a poem: for example, by poem structure or by theme.

Look at some ideas one student has noted in response to the exam-style question on page 49. These ideas are in '**chronological order**': the order in which they appear in the poem.

A strawberries – red, heart-shaped – suggest love ....

B heat of summer described: 'sultry afternoon' – passion? ....

C 'feast' contrasts with simple plate of strawberries – suggests simple pleasures transformed by love ....

D image of forks crossed – reflects the closeness of the couple ....

E 'heat intense / and summer lightning' – suggests heat has built to dramatic passion ....

F final line – form and word choice emphasise focus on love, not cleaning up after feast ....

(1) The student could organise their ideas by **structure**, dividing the poem into three stages:

1. **Beginning:** first impressions	
2. **Middle:** how key ideas/events develop	
3. **End:** final impressions in the final lines	

Organise the points in the student's plan by adding ✎ the letters **A** to **F** to the table above.

(2) The student could, instead, choose to organise their ideas by **theme**. For example:

<u>Weather</u>   <u>Strawberries</u>   <u>Love</u>

a Label ✎ points **A** to **F** in the student's list above to show which of these three themes it belongs to.

b In what order would you sequence the three themes?
  • Look at the points above. Which **point** do you think should come first? Would this be a good **theme** to focus on first?
  • Now think about which of the other two themes would follow the first more logically.
  • Finally, check you can link the remaining theme to the second theme.

  Tick ✓ one of the plans below, or write ✎ your own.

A	1. weather	B	1. strawberries	C	1. love	D	1. ....
	2. love		2. weather		2. strawberries		2. ....
	3. strawberries		3. love		3. weather		3. ....

(3) Which method do you think would be most effective in this case? Circle Ⓐ **one**.

by structure   by theme

Writing about one poem

To write an effective response to the first part of the exam question focusing on one poem, you need to:
- annotate the poem, thinking about how the poet's choices have shaped your understanding and response to it
- explore how the poet's choices work together in the quotations you select
- structure your response carefully and logically.

Look at one student's annotations of the poem 'Strawberries', written in response to the exam-style question you saw at the start of the unit.

Exam-style question

In 'Strawberries', how does the speaker present his thoughts and feelings? (24 marks)

	Quotation	Annotation	
A	facing each other / your knees held in mine	emphasises closeness of speaker and his lover	☐
B	strawberries glistening / in the hot sunlight	strawberries described like jewels / hot = passion	☐
C	sweet in that air	thinks strawberries or his lover are sweet? Or both?	☐
D	your eager mouth	suggests lover feels the same passion as the speaker	☐
E	lean back again / let me love you	command verbs/short lines emphasise strength of his feeling?	☐
F	let the sun beat / on our forgetfulness	suggests heat of the day and the heat of their passion / blanks out everything else / suggests both speaker and his lover share that feeling	☐

1. Which points are relevant to the exam-style question: that is, which points focus on the speaker's thoughts and feelings? Tick ✓ them.

2. Which of the points you have ticked would allow the student to make significant comments on the poet's choices of language, structure and form? Highlight 🖊 the relevant letters.

3. How would you sequence the points you have selected – by theme or by structure? Write 🖊 the letters of the points you have ticked and highlighted **in order** below to show how you would sequence them in your response.

....

Your turn!

You are now going to **begin planning your answer** in response to the exam-style question.

Exam-style question

In 'Strawberries', how does the speaker present his thoughts and feelings?   **(24 marks)**

(1) Review your annotations of the poem on page 50. Which of your ideas are relevant to the exam-style question? Note 🖉 them below.

....

....

....

....

....

....

....

....

....

....

....

....

....

....

....

....

....

....

....

....

(2) Which of the points you have noted will allow you to make the most significant, detailed comments on the poet's choices of language, structure and form? Tick ✓ them.

(3) How will you sequence the points you have selected – by **theme** or by **structure**? Number 🖉 the points you have ticked to show how you will sequence them in your response.

(4) Write 🖉 your response to the exam-style question on paper.

Review your skills

Check up

Review your response to the exam-style question on page 55. Tick ✓ the column to show how well you think you have done each of the following.

	Not quite ✓	Nearly there ✓	Got it! ✓
selected relevant points	☐	☐	☐
structured points carefully and logically	☐	☐	☐
commented on the poet's choices of language, form and structure	☐	☐	☐

Need more practice?

Here is another exam-style question, this time relating to 'When You Are Old' by William Butler Yeats which you can find on page 73.

Exam-style question

In 'When You Are Old', how does the poet present the speaker's feelings? **(24 marks)**

Plan and write 🖉 your response to the exam-style question.
You'll find some suggested points to refer to in the Answers section.

> You may have done some work on this poem in Unit 1.

Comparison practice

Here is another exam-style question, relating to **both** 'Strawberries' by Edwin Morgan **and** 'When You Are Old' by William Butler Yeats.

Exam-style question

In both 'Strawberries' and 'When You Are Old', the speakers talk about relationships. What are the similarities and/or differences between the ways the poets present relationships? **(8 marks)**

Write 🖉 **one** or **two** paragraphs in response to the exam-style question, **comparing** 'Strawberries' and 'When You Are Old'.

How confident do you feel about each of these **skills?** Colour 🖉 in the bars.

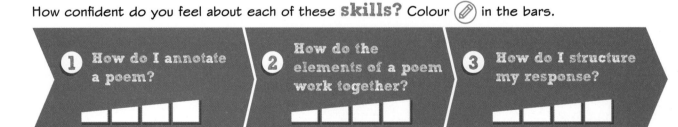

1 How do I annotate a poem?

2 How do the elements of a poem work together?

3 How do I structure my response?

Read, understand and respond to texts (AO1); Analyse the language, form and structure used by a writer to create meanings and effects (AO2)

⑧ Comparing poems

This unit will help you to compare the ways in which a similar theme or idea is presented in two poems. The skills you will build are to:

- identify relevant and significant similarities and differences in two poems
- develop a comparison of two poems
- structure a comparison of two poems.

In the exam you will face a question like the one below. This is about the poems on the next page. At the end of the unit you will **plan and write your response** to this question.

Exam-style question

In both 'Poem' and 'My Grandfather's Garden' the speakers describe thoughts and feelings after someone has died. What are the similarities and/or differences between the ways the poets present those thoughts and feelings? **(8 marks)**

Before you tackle the question you will work through three key questions in the **skills boosts** to help you compare two poems.

 ① How do I plan my comparison?   **② How do I develop my comparison?**   **③ How do I structure my comparison?**

Read both poems on the next page. In Paper 2, Section C of your English Literature exam, you will write about one unseen poem, then compare it with another unseen poem.

As you read each poem, think about: ⊘

what you learn about the speaker in the poem and the person who has died	the speaker's thoughts and feelings about the person who has died	the speaker's thoughts and feelings following the person's death.
☐	☐	☐

My Grandfather's Garden

Where bloodshot apples peered from the grass
and seed packets taught me the patience
of waiting through a season.

Where I cracked the seams of pods,
5   and fired out peas with a thumbnail
pushed along the down of the soft inside.

Where he kept order with hoe prods,
at the stems of lettuces, emerging like
overgrown moth-eaten flowers, colours drained.

10   Where I crouched on the shed's corrugate roof,
touching ripe damsons, which fell into the lap
of my stretched T-shirt.

Where I have come now, a month after his death,
the house and garden following him out of my life,
15   to cut back brambles and pack away tools.

Where, entering the hollow socket of the shed,
I hear damsons tap the roof,
telling me there is no one to catch them.

Owen Sheers

Poem

And if it snowed and snow covered the drive
he took a spade and tossed it to one side.
And always tucked his daughter up at night
And **slippered** her the one time that she lied.
5   And every week he tipped up half his wage.
And what he didn't spend each week he saved.
And praised his wife for every meal she made.
And once, for laughing, punched her in the face.

And for his mum he hired a private nurse.
10   And every Sunday taxied her to church.
And he blubbed when she went from bad to worse.
And twice he lifted ten quid from her purse.

Here's how they rated him when they looked back:
sometimes he did this, sometimes he did that.

Simon Armitage

slippered: to be physically punished by being beaten with a slipper

1   a   Which **one** line or image in each poem reveals most about the person who has died and/or the speaker's thoughts and feelings about them? Underline Ⓐ it.

   b   For each poem, write 🖉 **one** or **two** sentences commenting on what is revealed or suggested in the lines or images you have underlined.

'My Grandfather's Garden': ....

....

....

....

'Poem': ....

....

....

....

1 How do I plan my comparison?

To begin planning your comparison, you need to think about the key ideas expressed in each poem.

1 Begin by focusing on the key ideas in each poem, looking at them one at a time.

Ask yourself:
- Who and/or what is the poem about?
- How is this idea or subject presented?
- What is the speaker's viewpoint: are they focusing on themselves, or on someone else?
- What kinds of thoughts and feelings are expressed?

a Now summarise your ideas, comparing the two poems by completing these sentences. 🖉

Both poems are about

....

....

However, 'My Grandfather's Garden' focuses on

....

....

whereas in 'Poem' the speaker describes

....

....

b Review the sentences you have written. Do they answer all the questions you asked yourself before you wrote them? If not, add 🖉 to your sentences.

2 Look at this list of key ideas and evidence from the two poems.

My Grandfather's Garden

a seed packets taught me the patience of waiting through a season.

b he kept order with hoe prods

c the house and garden following him out of my life

Key ideas

A Details of the life of the person who has died.

B The speaker's thoughts and feelings about the person who has died.

C The speaker's thoughts and feelings about their death.

Poem

d And praised his wife for every meal she made. And once, for laughing, punched her in the face.

e And he blubbed when she went from bad to worse. And twice he lifted ten quid from her purse.

f Here's how they rated him when they looked back: sometimes he did this, sometimes he did that.

a Draw 🖉 lines to link each key idea to relevant evidence from each poem.

b Compare each key idea in the two poems. Is it a similarity or a difference? For each key idea, circle Ⓐ either **S** for Similarity or **D** for difference.

Key idea A: S   D

Key idea B: S   D

Key idea C: S   D

② How do I develop my comparison?

To develop your comparison of two poems you can:
- compare key ideas and how the poets present them in their choice of language, form and structure
- compare similar uses of language, form and structure in the poems and impacts that these have.

① Both poems create an impression of the person who has died. Compare these two pieces of evidence.

My Grandfather's Garden

> he kept order with hoe prods

Poem

> And praised his wife for every meal she made.
> And once, for laughing, punched her in the face.

a Identify **one** word or phrase in each quotation that creates the strongest impression of the person who has died. Circle Ⓐ it.

b What impression does this word or phrase create? Complete ✏️ the sentences below to explain your ideas, crossing out ~~cat~~ one of the highlighted words as appropriate.

In 'My Grandfather's Garden', the speaker presents his grandfather as

....

....

....

Similarly/However, in 'Poem', the speaker creates the impression that the man who has died

....

....

② In addition to comparing the key ideas in the poems, you can compare the poets' choices of language, form and structure and the impact of those choices. Use some or all of the words and phrases below to compare ✏️ as many of the poets' choices as you can.

For more help on language, form and structure, see Units 3–6.

In	both poems	'My Grandfather's Garden'	'Poem'
the poet uses	repetition	rhyme and end-stopped lines	enjambment
of	the word 'Where'	the word 'And'	
to emphasise	the different events in a life	the importance of this place	a key idea
to create	a slow pace	a fast pace	
and	a quiet, reflective mood	an abrupt, aggressive mood	
similarly	however	in the same way	whereas

....

....

....

....

....

③ How do I structure my comparison?

In each paragraph of your comparison, aim to compare the **key ideas** in the poem and how they are conveyed, exploring and comparing the **poets' choices** of language, form and structure.

① Look at the sentences below. They are from one paragraph of a student's response comparing 'My Grandfather's Garden' and 'Poem'.

Writing about both poems

A Both poems focus on the death of a person.

B 'My Grandfather's Garden' focuses on the speaker's thoughts and feelings after his grandfather's death, whereas 'Poem' focuses on everything a man did in his life and how people judged him.

C The poet uses enjambment throughout 'My Grandfather's Garden' whereas each line of 'Poem' is end-stopped with a rhyme.

Writing about 'My Grandfather's Garden'

D In 'My Grandfather's Garden', the speaker focuses more on his memories of the time he spent in the garden than on his memories of his grandfather, which shows how important this place was to him.

E The speaker describes his grandfather's shed using the metaphor of a 'hollow socket', suggesting that it feels empty because his grandfather is not in it any more, which highlights the speaker's feeling of loss and emptiness at his death.

F In 'My Grandfather's Garden', the use of enjambment creates a slow pace and a reflective mood that emphasise the huge impact of his grandfather's death on the speaker.

Writing about 'Poem'

G In 'Poem', the speaker contrasts the good and bad aspects of the man's life, for example how the man 'praised' his wife but also 'punched her in the face'.

H However, the bad aspects are described after the good, using slang and aggressive language choices, which make the bad aspects stand out more than the good.

I In 'Poem', the use of rhyme and end-stopped lines create a strong rhythm, a fast pace and a tone that suggest the speaker does not think any of these things are very important.

ⓐ Which sentences focus on a **key idea**? Label ✏ them **K**.

ⓑ Which sentences focus on the **poets' choices** of language, form or structure? Label ✏ them **C**.

ⓒ Which sentences would you include in a paragraph comparing the two poems? Tick ✓ them.

ⓓ Number ✏ the sentences you have ticked to show how you would sequence them in a paragraph.

Comparing poems

To write an effective comparison of two poems, you need to:

- identify and compare the key ideas in the poems
- develop your comparison, exploring and comparing the poets' choices of language, form and structure
- structure each paragraph of your response to make a careful, developed comparison of the two poems.

Now look at this exam-style question, which you saw at the start of the unit.

Exam-style question

In both 'Poem' and 'My Grandfather's Garden' the speakers describe thoughts and feelings after someone has died. What are the similarities and/or differences between the ways the poets present those thoughts and feelings? (8 marks)

Read the paragraph below, written by a student in response to this exam-style question.

> The poets create very different impressions of the people who have died. In 'My Grandfather's Garden', the impression is created of a quiet, organised man who 'kept order' in his garden and because he is not really described it seems like you might not even notice him. In 'Poem' though, the man's life is listed in lots of detail, making him seem violent and dishonest. He once 'slippered' his daughter and 'punched his wife'. The poet emphasises how unfair and horrible the man is by showing why he did this – his wife laughed and his daughter told just one lie. Both poets use the form of the poem to add to these impressions: in 'Poem' the rhyme and repetition of 'And' create a fast, aggressive pace, reflecting the aggression of the man described, whereas the enjambment and irregular lines in 'My Grandfather's Garden' create a quiet, reflective mood as the speaker remembers his quiet grandfather and the time he spent in his garden.

(1) Annotate the paragraph, underlining (A) and labelling (🖉) A to H the parts of the paragraph in which this student has achieved the key features below.

Focusing on both poems	Focusing on 'My Grandfather's Garden'	Focusing on 'Poem'
A identifies a significant similarity or difference B compares poets' choices	C identifies a key idea D evidence to support key idea E comments on effect of poet's choices	F identifies a key idea G evidence to support key idea H comments on effect of poet's choices

Your turn!

You are now going to **plan and write your response** to the exam-style question.

Exam-style question

In both 'Poem' and 'My Grandfather's Garden' the speakers describe thoughts and feelings after someone has died. What are the similarities and/or differences between the ways the poets present those thoughts and feelings?   **(8 marks)**

1 Use the space below to plan **three paragraphs** in response to the question.

   a Note ✏ **three** similarities or differences in the ways the poets present their thoughts and feelings after someone has died. You could focus on comparing:

   - the key ideas in the poems
   - the poets' choices of language, form and structure.

   b For each similarity or difference, note ✏ relevant evidence from each poem. This could be a quotation, a description of the poem's form or structure, a poetic device, etc.

   c Annotate ✏ your evidence, noting the effect of the poets' choices of language and/or form and/or structure.

Similarity or Difference	Evidence: 'My Grandfather's Garden'	Evidence: 'Poem'

2 Now write ✏ your response to the exam-style question above on paper.

Review your skills

Check up

Review your response to the exam-style question on page 63. Tick ✓ the column to show how well you think you have done each of the following.

	Not quite ✓	Nearly there ✓	Got it! ✓
identified significant similarities and/or differences	☐	☐	☐
explored the poets' choices of language, form and structure	☐	☐	☐
structured my paragraphs effectively	☐	☐	☐

Need more practice?

Here is another exam-style question, this time relating to a comparison of 'My Grandfather's Garden', which can be found on page 58 and 'When You Are Old' on page 73.

Exam-style question

In both 'My Grandfather's Garden' and 'When You Are Old' the speakers show feelings of loss. What are the similarities and/or differences between the ways the poets present those feelings?

(8 marks)

Plan and write ✏ your response to this exam-style question. You'll find some suggested points to refer to in the Answers section.

How confident do you feel about each of these **skills?** Colour ✏ in the bars.

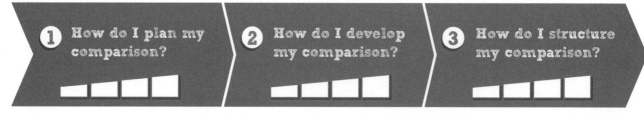

1 How do I plan my comparison?

2 How do I develop my comparison?

3 How do I structure my comparison?

Expressing your ideas clearly and precisely

This unit will help you to express your response to unseen poems as clearly and precisely as possible. The skills you will build are to:

- select vocabulary to express your ideas precisely
- link your ideas to express them clearly
- extend your sentences to develop ideas more fully.

In the exam you will face questions like the one below. This is about the poem on the next page. At the end of the unit you will **write one paragraph** in response to this question.

Exam-style question

In 'On Children', how does the speaker present his thoughts about being a parent?   **(24 marks)**

Before you tackle the question you will work through three key questions in the **skills boosts** to help you develop a critical writing style.

1 How do I choose vocabulary which expresses my ideas precisely?

2 How can I link my ideas to express them more clearly?

3 How can I extend my sentences to develop my ideas more fully?

Read the poem on the next page. In Paper 2, Section C of your English Literature exam, you will write about one unseen poem, then compare it with another unseen poem.

As you read the poem, think about:

who the speaker in the poem is talking to	the key ideas and advice the speaker gives the reader	why the reader might want or need the speaker's advice.

On Children

Your children are not your children.
They are the sons and daughters of Life's longing for itself.
They come through you but not from you,
And though they are with you yet they belong not to you.

5   You may give them your love but not your thoughts,
For they have their own thoughts.
You may house their bodies but not their souls,
For their souls dwell in the house of tomorrow,
which you cannot visit, not even in your dreams.
10 You may strive to be like them,
but seek not to make them like you.
For life goes not backward nor **tarries** with yesterday.

You are the bows from which your children
as living arrows are sent forth.
15 The archer sees the mark upon the path of the infinite,
and He bends you with His might
that His arrows may go swift and far.
Let your bending in the archer's hand be for gladness;
For even as He loves the arrow that flies,
20 so He loves also the bow that is stable.

Khalil Gibran

tarries: remains, waits around, delays leaving somewhere

(1) In the table below, note 🖊 some of the advice given in the poem.

What parents *should not do*	What parents *should do*
•	•
•	•
•	•

(2) Write 🖊 **one** or **two** sentences summing up the key ideas in the poem.

66   **Unit 9 Expressing your ideas clearly and precisely**

1 How do I choose vocabulary which expresses my ideas precisely?

When you write and review your response to a poem, or compare two poems, think about synonyms you could use to make your description of the poet's intention and choices more precise.

synonym: a word with a similar meaning, e.g. large, big, huge, vast, etc.

(1) Look again at the poem 'On Children' on page 66. Read it aloud or, as you read it to yourself, try to hear your voice 'inside your head'.

How would you describe the **pace** of the poem? Circle (A) **one** or **two** words below, or add (✎) your own ideas. You could use a thesaurus to help you.

slow	lethargic		regular	even		fast	hurried
hesitant	plodding		measured	steady		rapid	energetic

(2) How would you describe the **mood** of the poem? Circle (A) **one** or **two** words below, or add (✎) your own ideas. You could use a thesaurus to help you.

angry	assertive	commanding	calm	reflective	anxious	happy	chaotic
aggressive	authoritative	certain	confident	melancholy	tense	joyous	excited

(3) Look again at your answers to questions (1) and (2). Write (✎) **one** or **two** sentences commenting on the pace and mood of the poem 'On Children'.

....

....

....

(4) How would you describe the **poet's intention** in the poem? Write (✎) **one** or **two** sentences using the phrases below.

| The poet's intention is to: |

| persuade the reader to | describe | create the impression that |

| explore ideas of | explore and express feelings of | take a surprisingly different look at |

| invite the reader to | think differently about | explore a significant moment in their life when |

....

....

....

....

2 How can I link my ideas to express them more clearly?

You can use conjunctions and adverbials to link your ideas, helping you to express your views more clearly and fluently.

Conjunctions			
and	but	when	after
before	although	because	whereas

Adverbials		
also	therefore	similarly
	in the same way	however

(1) Look at the conjunctions and adverbials above. Add (✐) each one to the table below, to show the kinds of idea they can link.

	link similar ideas	link contrasting ideas	link explanations or consequences	indicate time or place
Conjunctions that can...				
Adverbials that can...				

(2) Rewrite (✐) the sentences below by:

EITHER

• using a **conjunction** to join the two sentences and **form one sentence**

OR:

• adding an **adverbial** to the second sentence **without joining them**.

For example:

Children have their own thoughts. Parents do not need to give them theirs.

(Because) children have their own thoughts, parents do not need to give them theirs.

Children have their own thoughts. (Therefore,) parents do not need to give them theirs.

a The speaker suggests that parents should not treat their children as possessions. He says, 'they belong not to you'.

....

....

b The speaker suggests that parents should be loving. They should not try to control or dominate their children.

....

....

c The poet contrasts what parents think with what children really are. He contrasts what parents should do with what they should not do.

....

....

3 How can I extend my sentences to develop my ideas more fully?

You can extend your sentences, and develop your ideas, by using:
- a present participle: a verb ending '-ing'
- the pronoun 'which'.

(1) You can use 'which' or a present participle to avoid repeatedly beginning sentences with 'This suggests...' or 'This shows...'. For example:

> Children are compared to 'living arrows'. (This) suggests they fly quickly and purposefully.

> Children are compared to 'living arrows', (which) suggests they fly quickly and purposefully.

> Children are compared to 'living arrows', (suggesting) they fly quickly and purposefully.

Change ✎ the sentences below into single sentences, using a present participle or 'which'.

a The speaker says that parents may 'house' their children's bodies. This highlights the role of parents in providing food and warmth for them.

....

....

b The speaker says that parents cannot 'visit' their children's souls 'even in your dreams'. This implies how different children and parents are.

....

....

(2) You can sometimes replace a conjunction with a present participle. For example:

> Parents are like a bow (because they send) their children out into the world.

> Parents are like a bow, (sending) their children out into the world.

Circle Ⓐ the conjunction in the sentences below. Replace ✎ the conjunction with a present participle.

a The poem shows how important it is to give children freedom and allow them to be themselves.

....

....

b The speaker highlights how parents feel the need to give children their thoughts and make them think the same as they do.

....

....

Expressing your ideas clearly and precisely

To express your ideas clearly and precisely, you can:

- select vocabulary that expresses your ideas precisely
- link your ideas using conjunctions, present participles, etc. to develop and express them clearly.

Now look at this exam-style question, which you saw at the start of the unit.

Exam-style question

In 'On Children', how does the speaker present his thoughts about being a parent?   **(24 marks)**

Look at this short paragraph from one student's response to the exam-style question.

> The speaker wants to get parents to think about how they treat their children. He describes parents as a bow that fires an arrow. He describes their children as the arrow. This shows how important the parents' job is. Without parents, children could not 'fly'. This shows that children need to be separate from their parents.

1. **a** Underline (A) **at least three** examples of vocabulary which could be more precise.
   b Note (✐) down in the margin **at least two** alternative vocabulary choices for each one.
   c Highlight (✐) any of the sentences which you feel should be linked or developed to improve the clarity and precision of the writing.
   d Write (✐) an improved version of this paragraph, either by adjusting the text above or by rewriting it in the space below.

....

....

....

....

....

....

....

Your turn!

You are now going to **write one paragraph** in response to the exam-style question.

Exam-style question

In 'On Children', how does the speaker present his thoughts about being a parent?   **(24 marks)**

(1) In your response, you could explore one or more of the key features of the poem. Add (✏) some ideas to **at least three** of the headings below.

(?) The poet's intention

(?) The key ideas in the poem

(?) Some of the poet's choices of language and/or poetic devices and their effect

(?) The poet's choice of form and structure and its effect

(?) The pace and mood of the poem

(2) Now add (✏) relevant evidence to support each of your ideas.

(3) Review the ideas and evidence you have noted. Which will you include and link in the one paragraph you are going to write in response to the exam-style question above? Tick (✓) them.

(4) Now write (✏) **one** paragraph on paper in response to the exam-style question above.

Remember to:
• choose your vocabulary carefully
• think about ways in which you can link your ideas to develop and express them clearly and precisely.

Review your skills

Check up

Review your response to the exam-style question on page 71. Tick ✓ the column to show how well you think you have done each of the following.

	Not quite ✓	Nearly there ✓	Got it! ✓
selected precise vocabulary	☐	☐	☐
linked and developed my ideas clearly and precisely using conjunctions, adverbials, present participles, etc.	☐	☐	☐

Need more practice?

You can EITHER:

1. Look again at your paragraph written in response to the exam-style question on page 71. Rewrite it, experimenting with different vocabulary choices and sentence structures, linking your ideas in different ways. Which are most effective in expressing your ideas clearly and precisely?

AND/OR:

2. Write a **second** paragraph in response to the exam-style question, using some more of the ideas you noted on page 71. Remember to focus closely on your vocabulary choices and sentence structures to express your ideas as clearly and precisely as possible.

Comparison practice

Here is another exam-style question, relating to **both** 'On Children' by Khalil Gibran **and** 'Mother to Son' by Langston Hughes on page 75.

Exam-style question

In both 'On Children' and 'Mother to Son', the speakers give advice. What are the similarities and/or differences between the ways the poets present this advice?   **(8 marks)**

Write one paragraph in response to the exam-style question. Focus on **expressing your ideas as clearly and precisely as possible.**

How confident do you feel about each of these skills? Colour in the bars.

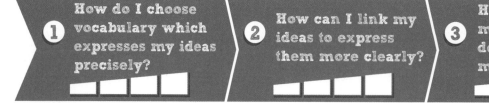

1. How do I choose vocabulary which expresses my ideas precisely?
2. How can I link my ideas to express them more clearly?
3. How can I extend my sentences to develop my ideas more fully?

More practice texts

When You Are Old

When you are old and grey and full of sleep,
And nodding by the fire, take down this book,
And slowly read, and dream of the soft look
Your eyes had once, and of their shadows deep;

5   How many loved your moments of glad grace,
And loved your beauty with love false or true,
But one man loved the pilgrim soul in you,
And loved the sorrows of your changing face;

And bending down beside the glowing bars,
10 Murmur, a little sadly, how Love fled
And paced upon the mountains overhead
And hid his face amid a crowd of stars.

William Butler Yeats

Legend

The rooms were mirrors
for that luminous face,
the morning windows ferned
with cold. Outside
5   a level world of snow.
Voiceless birds in the trees
like notes in the books
in the piano stool.
She let us suck top-of-the-milk
10   burst from the bottles like corks.
Then wrapped shapeless
we stumped to the park
between the parapets of snow
in the wake of the shovellers,
15   cardboard rammed in the tines of garden forks.
The lake was an empty rink
and I stepped out,
pushing my sister first
onto its creaking floor.
20   When I brought her home,
shivering, wailing, soaked,
they thought me a hero.
But I still wake at night,
to hear the Snow Queen's knuckles crack,
25   black water running fingers through the ice.

Gillian Clarke

Mother to Son

Well, son, I'll tell you:
Life for me ain't been no crystal stair.
It's had tacks in it,
And splinters,
5   And boards torn up,
And places with no carpet on the floor—
Bare.
But all the time
I'se been a-climbin' on,
10   And reachin' landin's,
And turnin' corners,
And sometimes goin' in the dark
Where there ain't been no light.
So boy, don't you turn back.
15   Don't you set down on the steps
'Cause you finds it's kinder hard.
Don't you fall now—
For I'se still goin', honey,
I'se still climbin',
20   And life for me ain't been no crystal stair.

Langston Hughes

A Letter in October

Dawn comes later and later now,
and I, who only a month ago
could sit with coffee every morning
watching the light walk down the hill
5   to the edge of the pond and place
a doe there, shyly drinking,

then see the light step out upon
the water, sowing reflections
to either side—a garden
10 of trees that grew as if by magic—
now see no more than my face,
mirrored by darkness, pale and odd,

startled by time. While I slept,
night in its thick winter jacket
15 bridled the doe with a twist
of wet leaves and led her away,
then brought its black horse with harness
that creaked like a cricket, and turned

the water garden under. I woke,
20 and at the waiting window found
the curtains open to my open face;
beyond me, darkness. And I,
who only wished to keep looking out,
must now keep looking in.

Ted Kooser

Answers

Unit 1

Page 2

2 A Jasmine, Gunpowder, Assam, Earl Grey and Ceylon are different types of tea. The phrase 'I love tea's names' is a useful clue.

B Mount Wu-Yi is a mountain in China where tea is grown. The phrase 'harvest the slopes' offers a clue.

Page 3

1 a Details could include: the speaker looking happy, her lover, a teapot, etc.

b For example: The speaker is in love and enjoys making tea for her lover.

d For example: 'I like pouring your tea'; 'I am your lover, smitten, straining your tea.'

Page 4

1 a For example: love, making tea

2 a For example:

Tea: Assam, Ceylon, china, cup, cupped, Earl Grey, fragrant, Gunpowder, harvest, Jasmine, leaves, liquid, milk, Mount Wu-Yi, pot, pouring, sip, slopes, straining, sugar, sweetest, tea, tipping

Love: eyes, half-smile, hands, heart, lips, love, lover, smitten, soul

3 a I, your, it, your, you're, I, your, you, you, your, I, I, I, your, your, I, I, you, I, it's, you, I, your, your

b For example: The most frequent pronoun used is 'you/your', followed closely by 'I' and then 'it', suggesting that the poet ('I') is oblivious to almost everything except the object of her poem – her new lover ('you'). Very little from the outside world intrudes on their love in the poem, except their mutual enjoyment of tea.

Page 5

1 The speaker directly addresses her lover, talking about her lover's fondness for tea, and her happiness in making tea for her lover.

2 The quotation suggests that the couple have not been together long, but that the speaker is entirely absorbed by her deep feelings of love.

3 The overriding impression is of the speaker's love. Little is revealed about her lover, other than their love of tea.

Page 6

2 D and E are least relevant to the focus of the question.

Page 8

Sample Need more practice responses:

- The speaker imagines someone he once loved has grown old.

- Suggests many admired this person for her physical beauty, but none loved them as deeply as the speaker.

- The speaker imagines this person is alone and lonely now love has 'fled'.

- Suggests the speaker may have feelings of bitterness; perhaps his love for this person was not recognised or returned.

Sample Comparison practice responses:

'Tea':

- Focuses on a current relationship.

- Focuses on strong feelings of love and happiness.

'When You Are Old':

- Focuses on a past relationship.

- Focuses on lost love and feelings of bitterness.

Unit 2

Page 10

1 a For example: four children go to a beach: Maggie finds a shell; Milly finds a starfish; Molly is chased by a crab; May finds a stone.

b For example: The poem focuses on the experiences of four children at the beach.

Page 11

1 For example: The words 'beach' and 'play' suggest the poem will describe four children happily playing at the seaside. It creates a positive image of fun and friendship.

2 For example: 'troubles' suggests Maggie may be troubled in some way; 'befriended' could suggest that Milly is lonely and finds it difficult to make friends; 'chased' suggests Molly may be fearful or nervous; 'alone' suggests May is familiar with loneliness.

3 There is a surprising connection made between the initial image of a group of children on a beach, and the four separate images of the children as isolated individuals, focusing on the difficulties they face.

Page 12

1 a For example: positive, optimistic, happy

b 'beach'; 'play'

2 a For example: unsettling, unsettled

b 'chased'; 'horrible'; 'alone'

Page 13

1 a For example:

A. 'went down to the beach (to play…'

B. 'couldn't remember her troubles', 'befriended a stranded star', 'chased', 'alone'

C. Verses 2–5 focus on each child, one at a time.

D. 'troubles', 'chased', 'alone'

E. 'couldn't remember her troubles', 'chased'

b A is the least developed; E is the most developed, giving the broadest response to the poem.

2 a For example:

Our responses to nature – and to life – reveal something about ourselves.

We can lose ourselves, and find out what we are truly like, by interacting with the natural world.

Page 14

1 **a** Both

    b Student A

    c Student B

Page 16

Sample Need more practice responses:

- Image of children protectively 'wrapped shapeless' from the cold contrasts with image of the speaker's sister saved from drowning, 'shivering, wailing, soaked'.
- Mood of excitement turns to fear and dramatic disaster: 'the Snow Queen's knuckles crack'.
- Feelings of guilt and fear are long-lasting: 'I still wake at night'.

Sample Comparison practice responses:

'maggie and milly and molly and may':

- Children are presented as individuals, playing separately.
- Childhood is a time of excitement and danger.
- The mood changes from positive to unsettling.

'Legend':

- The speaker and her sister are presented as a pair, referred to as 'us' and 'we', until the accident.
- Childhood is a time of excitement and danger.
- The mood changes from excitement to dramatic disaster.

Unit 3

Page 18

1 Get up, eat cereal, walk the dog, work, lie down with their mate, eat dinner, sleep.

Page 19

1 **a** Time

    b 'I got out of bed', 'cereal', 'All morning', 'At noon', 'ate dinner', 'slept', 'another day'

    c The poet describes the events in a typical day of her life from waking up until going to sleep.

2 **a** The last two lines: lines 25–6

    b A sudden reversal: the speaker effectively dismisses the happiness of the preceding lines by sharply shifting her focus to a different, potentially less pleasant future.

Page 20

1 The poem is mainly focused on the thoughts and feelings of the speaker.

2 For example:

- the actual past: 'I got out of bed'
- a possible past: 'It might have been otherwise'
- a definite future: 'it will be otherwise'

3 **a** 'It might have been otherwise.'

    b For example:

        The repetition emphasises her awareness of how her life could have turned out differently, implying that she feels fortunate.

4 **a/b** The speaker contrasts her life now with her life in the future, highlighting that she expects significant change.

Page 21

1–**5** All responses are potentially valid.

Page 22

identifies a key idea in the poem	The speaker gives a strong impression that she thinks she is very fortunate in her life.
supports key idea with evidence	for example, it begins when she 'got out of bed' and then 'ate cereal' and it ends as she 'slept in a bed' ...for example, she has 'two strong legs', suggesting she is healthy, and she has 'silver candlesticks', suggesting she has wealth.
identifies a structural element or feature	The poem is structured around the events of a typical day in her life... After each of these events, she repeats the phrase 'It might have been otherwise'.
comments on the effect of the poet's structural choice	Each of these events highlights a positive aspect of her life:
comments on how the effect of the structural choice supports the poet's intention	The poem's structure and the use of repetition strongly imply how grateful she feels that everything she does and has in her life makes her happy and comfortable and that she can choose how she spends and enjoys her days.

Page 24

Sample Need more practice responses:

- Focuses on the speaker's past and present and her son's future: written in the first person, directly addressed to her son.
- Contrasts image of life as a 'crystal stair' with the reality of her life: 'tacks', 'splinters', 'boards torn up', 'no carpet'.
- Repetition of 'life for me ain't been no crystal stair' in final line emphasises speaker's key idea: her life has been difficult.

Sample Comparison practice responses:

'Mother to Son':

- Focuses on past, then present, then future.
- Repetition in final line suggests past and future will not differ.

'Otherwise':

- Focuses on present, then future.
- Repetition of 'It might have been otherwise' contrasted with 'it will be otherwise' in final line suggests the present and the future will differ.

Unit 4

Page 26

1 For example, possible impressions include:

the city: a: dilapidated: 'abandoned to crisp packets and cans'. **b:** busy: 'men and women are lost in transactions'

people who live in the city: a: focused on making money: 'the deal is done'. **b:** isolated: 'a new mother stands on her doorstep and blinks'

the lilacs that grow in the city: a: resilient: 'in all these places the city lilacs are pushing / their cones of blossom into the spring'. b: beautiful: 'sweet, wild perfume'

Page 27

1. (a) The city
   (b) For example: ugly, dirty, miserable
2. (b) For example: 'crack-haunted', 'sour', 'wheelie bin'
3. (a) The people in the city
   (b) For example: busy, isolated, cold, miserable
   (c) For example: 'men', 'urgent', 'girls shiver', 'new mother', 'blinks'

Page 28

1. All are arguable.
2. For example:

   rich: wealth, fertility, growth

   sweet: appealing, delicious, productive

   poor: poverty, infertility, low quality

   starved: mistreated, thin, weak
3. For example: The description 'sour earth' suggests the soil in the city is spoilt and rotten and that nothing can grow there.
4. For example: 'urgent' suggests fast-paced, desperate, anxious; 'shiver' suggests cold, fear, discomfort.

Page 29

1. (a) vague: E
      describe: A
   (b) effect: C, D
      intention: B
2. vague: D
   describe: B
   effect: A
   intention: C, E

Page 30

identifies a key idea in the poem	The poet then contrasts her description of a broken and neglected city with her description of the lilacs that grow there.
identifies a significant language choice	She describes the lilacs 'pushing' their way into the city
comments on the connotations/effect of language choice	which suggests their strength and power as though it takes a massive effort to squeeze into this crowded and unwelcoming place
comments on how language choice supports the poet's intention	giving the impression of nature as powerful and something that will always survive. This strength of nature makes the city seem a better place, as though there is life and strength, not just loneliness and decay.

Page 32

Sample Need more practice responses:
- Vivid, appealing description of the life of late summer: 'light', 'reflections', 'garden ... magic', which the speaker sits passively enjoying 'with coffee every morning', suggests appreciation of the place where he lives.
- Contrast with negative images of autumn's lifeless, cold, wet darkness: 'thick winter jacket', 'wet leaves', 'darkness' suggests feelings of dissatisfaction with the place where he lives.
- Forces the speaker to focus on 'my face', reflected in darkness: 'pale and odd'; suggests he is isolated in his house, cut off from the world outside.

Sample Comparison practice responses:

'City Lilacs':
- Positive language contrasts the power of the natural world: 'city lilacs ... pushing / their cones of blossom into the spring', 'sweet, wild perfume', with negative images of city life: 'crack-haunted alleys', 'sour earth'.

'A Letter in October':
- Contrasts positive language describing light and life of late summer with negative language describing darkness and cold of October.

Unit 5

Page 34

1. 'A regularly repeated sequence of activities' is implied in the final stanza.

Page 35

1. For example:

   A: 'splashed': onomatopoeia; 'splashed', 'swaying', 'stems': alliteration

   B: 'humps of the honeybees': alliteration and assonance
2. Adds emphasis; makes the description more vivid; you can hear and see what the poet is describing, giving greater sensory immediacy to the image.
3. (b) For example: The soft alliterative sounds in these lines create a peaceful, quiet mood suggesting the sound of splashing water / a gentle breeze.
4. Adds emphasis; links two words to highlight a surprising image.

Page 36

1. 'splashed': metaphor
2. For example: The image gives the light a feeling of fluidity, refreshing and giving life to the plants.
3. (a) For example: romance, affection, intimacy, gentle
   (b) The image suggests the gentle, loving affection of the light landing on the roses.

Page 37

1. (a) vague: C, D
      describe: A
   (b) effect: B
      intention: E
2. vague: B
   describe: A
   effect: C, D
   intention: E

Page 38

identifies a key idea in the poem	*In the second part of the poem, the speaker goes into his house to finish a poem about his experience in the garden …describes the place he goes to write the poem in very negative terms.*
identifies a poetic device	*He uses the metaphor of a 'cell' to describe it… He describes his view of a compost heap as a 'steamy old stinkpile'. The alliteration of the letter 's' in this description…*
comments on the effect of a poetic device	*…suggesting it is small and like being in prison. …almost suggests the hiss of the stinking fumes wafting up from the compost heap and floating in through his window.*
comments on how poetic devices support the poet's intention	*Both of these images use poetic devices to emphasise the difference between his experience inside the house, writing about the beauty of nature, compared with his experience outside the house, actually enjoying the beauty of nature.*

Page 40

Sample Need more practice responses:

- Light personified: 'watching the light walk down the hill'
- Darkness personified in opposition to light: 'brought its black horse', 'turned / the water garden under'
- Onomatopoeia/alliteration/simile of 'creaked like a cricket' creates powerful image of darkness.

Sample Comparison practice responses:

'The Round':

- The natural world/light presented as life-giving, creating a peaceful, quiet mood.

'A Letter in October':

- The natural world in autumn presented as the loss of light/beauty to the power of darkness.

Unit 6

Page 42

(1) Last day of summer: 'the day the summer went', 'wind and dark still forage at my door'

(2) Stanzas 1–4

(3) Stanzas 5–8

(4) A, C, E (e.g. 'road… toad'; 'happened… opened'), G ('I saw…')

Page 43

(1) A, B: regular form; C, D, E, F: free verse

(2) For example: The use of repetition at the start of stanzas 1–4 emphasises the impression of a series of snapshots. This pattern of repetition and description ends, and the mood changes in stanzas 5–8 as the poet reflects on what she has seen.

Page 44

(1) (a) Taking out the rhyme changes the mood.

Changing the rhythm changes the mood, pace and emphasis.

(b) The regular rhythm and use of rhyme help to create a calm, even pace, suggesting a very reflective mood.

(2) For example:

The use of enjambment in the last four stanzas:

- changes the pace of the poem, making it faster.
- changes the mood of the poem, making it more anxious / less reflective.
- gives emphasis to the phrase 'or hate'.

Page 45

(1) For example:

In the first part of the poem:

the poet uses a regular stanza form | to create a series of scenes or snapshots

the poet uses a regular rhythm and rhyme | to create a regular, even pace | to create a reflective, thoughtful mood

In the second part of the poem:

the poet uses enjambment | to suggest the patterns of everyday speech | to create a faster pace | to suggest that the speaker's thoughts are suddenly racing.

(2) For example:

A: free verse, no regular rhythm, enjambment, short lines, no rhyme, a faster pace

M: a regular stanza form, a regular rhythm, longer lines, some rhyme and half rhyme, a slower pace

C: a regular stanza form, a regular rhythm, short lines, some rhyme and half rhyme, a faster pace

Page 46

(1) (a) Students A, B and C have all identified significant features of form.

(b) Student A's comments are vague and undeveloped. Comments on the 'flow' of a poem, and evaluation of the effect as 'quite effective' without explanation of how or why, are largely meaningless.

Students B and C effectively develop their comments on the effect of the poet's use of form and the contribution to the poet's intention.

Page 48

Sample Need more practice responses:

- Regular line length/stanza form and enjambment create a slower pace and reflective mood.
- Contrasting repetition of 'looking out', 'looking in' mirrors the change from light to darkness, summer to autumn.

Sample Comparison practice responses:

'Postcard':

- Short stanzas, rhyme and regular rhythm create a series of separate images or 'snapshots'.
- Final end-stopped line, contrasting with enjambment, highlights the final image of 'wind and dark'.

'A Letter in October':

- Longer stanzas and enjambment create a reflective mood as the speaker observes the changing season.
- Final end-stopped line, contrasting with enjambment, highlights the final image of the speaker's reflection in his window 'looking in'.

Unit 7

Page 50

① All responses are valid if supported by a valid explanation.

Page 51

① For example: The speaker and his lover eat strawberries on a hot day and are consumed by passion.

② ⓐ For example: 'your knees held in mine'

③ ⓐ For example: strawberries are red and heart-shaped, reflecting the theme of love/passion.

ⓑ For example: The image reflects the closeness of the couple.

④ ⓐ For example: The ideas in the poem are presented as brief 'snapshots' that cumulatively build an image of the scene, and the speaker's relationship with his lover.

ⓑ For example: The final line/stanza is given additional emphasis.

Page 52

① For example: This could suggest the speaker's lover is helpless in his arms because of their love for him. It makes his lover seem vulnerable but comfortable in this situation.

② For example: The poet's choice of language and structure emphasises the power of the sun. This shows the strength of the speaker's passion because it distracts him from the fierce heat of the sun.

Page 53

① For example:

Beginning: A, B, C

Middle: D, E

End: F

② ⓐ Weather: B, E

Strawberries: A, C

Love: D, F

ⓑ All responses are arguable.

③ Both responses are arguable.

Page 54

① All are arguably relevant; however, point 'C' is not immediately relevant, and point 'D' focuses more on the speaker's lover's feelings than on the speaker's.

② Annotations to A, B, E and F show the most developed comments on the poet's choices.

③ For example:

Structure:

Beginning: A

Middle: B, C, E

End: F

Theme:

Closeness: A, C

Passion: B, E, F

Page 56

Sample Need more practice responses:

- Compares people who love physical beauty with deeper admiration of a 'pilgrim soul' and 'sorrows', suggesting true love goes beyond the physical.

- Suggests that love based on physical attraction is temporary: it 'fled' and 'hid his face'.

- Suggests that a lost love can be regretted for the rest of a person's life.

Sample Comparison practice responses:

'Strawberries':

- Focuses on an afternoon of passion.

- Focuses on the happiness of a close relationship.

- Suggests love is more powerful than any other thought or feeling.

'When You Are Old':

- Focuses on the impact of love on an entire lifetime.

- Explores the feelings of a rejected lover.

- Suggests feelings of love can be 'false or true'.

Unit 8

Page 58

① ⓑ For example:

'My Grandfather's Garden': 'Where he kept order with hoe prods' suggests a man who cared for his garden methodically and carefully; 'the house and garden following him out of my life' suggests the speaker feels his loss keenly.

'Poem': 'And praised his wife for every meal she made / And once, for laughing, punched her in the face' suggests this man's unpredictable behaviour: a seemingly loving and grateful man with an unforgivably violent, irrational temper.

Page 59

① For example:

Both poems are about someone who has died.

However, 'My Grandfather's Garden' focuses on the memories of the speaker in the poem, suggesting feelings of loss and sadness at the death of his quiet, patient grandfather,

whereas in 'Poem' the speaker describes both the good and bad things that an anonymous man did in his life, suggesting his violence and dishonesty, but the speaker expresses no emotions at his death.

② ⓐ A: b, d, e

B: a

C: c, f

ⓑ All are differences.

Page 60

① ⓐ 'kept order'; 'punched her in the face'

ⓑ For example:

In 'My Grandfather's Garden', the speaker presents his grandfather as an organised man who spent his time working in his garden to grow fruit and vegetables.

However, in 'Poem', the speaker creates the impression that the man who has died was aggressive and short-tempered, with little respect for his wife.

(2) For example:

In 'My Grandfather's Garden' the poet uses repetition of the word 'Where' to emphasise the importance of this place whereas in 'Poem' the poet uses repetition of the word 'And' to emphasise the different events in a life.

In 'My Grandfather's Garden' the poet uses enjambment to create a slow pace and a quiet reflective mood. However, in 'Poem', the poet uses rhyme and end-stopped lines to create a fast pace and an abrupt, aggressive mood.

Page 61

(1) (a) A, B, D, G focus on key ideas.

(b) C, E, F, H, I focus on the poets' choices.

(c) All are valid.

(d) For example: A, B, D, E, G, H, C, F, I

Page 62

(1) A The poets create very different impressions of the people who have died.

B Both poets use the form of the poem to add to these impressions:

…in 'Poem' the rhyme and repetition of 'And' create a fast, aggressive pace, reflecting the aggression of the man described, whereas the enjambment and irregular lines in 'My Grandfather's Garden' create a quiet, reflective mood as the speaker remembers his quiet grandfather and the time he spent in his garden.

C In 'My Grandfather's Garden', the impression is created of a quiet, organised man

D who 'kept order' in his garden and because he is not really described

E it seems like you might not even notice him.

F In 'Poem' though, the man's life is listed in lots of detail, making him seem violent and dishonest.

G He once 'slippered' his daughter and 'punched his wife'.

H The poet emphasises how unfair and horrible the man is by showing why he did this – his wife laughed and his daughter told just one lie.

Page 64

Sample Need more practice responses:

'My Grandfather's Garden':

- Series of vivid memories of time spent in this garden, looking back over the past.
- Focuses on the speaker's thoughts and feelings.
- Highlights the speaker's sense of loss: 'the house and garden following him out of my life', 'hollow socket'.

'When You Are Old':

- An imagined future, inviting a former love to look back over the past.
- Focuses on the imagined thoughts and feelings of the former lover.
- Highlights the speaker's feelings of loss: 'how Love fled'.

Unit 9

Page 66

(1) For example:

What parents should not do: try to make children think the same way as them; try to restrict or contain their children's 'souls'; try to make their children like themselves.

What parents should do: give children their love; 'house their bodies'; try to be like their children.

(2) Parents should love and nurture their children but not try to control or mould them.

Page 67

(1) For example: regular, measured

(2) For example: confident, authoritative

(3) For example: The poet creates a regular, measured pace resulting in a confident, authoritative mood.

(4) For example: The poet's intention is to persuade the reader to think differently about the role of being a parent.

Page 68

(1)

	link similar ideas	link contrasting ideas	link explanations or consequences	indicate time or place
Conjunctions that can…	and	but although whereas	because	when after before
Adverbials that can…	also similarly in the same way	however	therefore	–

(2) For example:

a The speaker suggests that parents should not treat their children as possessions <u>because/when</u> he says, 'they belong not to you'.

b The speaker suggests that parents should be loving <u>but</u> they should not try to control or dominate their children.

The speaker suggests that parents should be loving. <u>However,</u> they should not try to control or dominate their children.

c The poet contrasts what parents think with what children really are, <u>and</u> what parents should do with what they should not do.

The poet contrasts what parents think with what children really are. <u>Similarly,</u> he contrasts what parents should do with what they should not do.

Page 69

(1) a The speaker says that parents may 'house' their children's bodies, <u>which highlights/highlighting</u> the role of parents in providing food and warmth for them.

b The speaker says that parents cannot 'visit' their children's souls 'even in your dreams', <u>which implies/implying</u> how different children and parents are.

(2) a The poem shows how important it is to give children freedom, ~~and~~ <u>allowing</u> them to be themselves.

b The speaker highlights how parents feel the need to give children their thoughts, ~~and~~ <u>making</u> them think the same as they do.

Page 70

(1) d For example:

In 'On Children', the speaker wants to ~~get~~ <u>encourage/persuade</u> parents to ~~think about~~ <u>consider/evaluate</u> how they treat their children. He describes parents as a bow that fires an arrow. ~~He describes~~ <u>and</u> their children as the arrow. ~~This shows,~~ showing how ~~important~~ <u>vital/essential</u> the parents' job is <u>because,</u> without parents, children could not 'fly'. This ~~shows~~ <u>suggests/implies</u> that children need to be separate from their parents.

Page 72

Sample Comparison practice responses:

'On Children':

- The speaker focuses on how parents should treat children.
- Advice is expressed authoritatively: 'you may', 'seek not'.
- The speaker uses the metaphor of a bow and arrow to highlight the roles of parent and child.

'Mother to Son':

- The speaker focuses on how children can learn from a parent.
- Advice is expressed authoritatively: 'don't you', 'don't you'.
- The speaker uses the metaphor of stairs to highlight life as an uphill climb.

Notes

LAPLAND

BONECHI

Project and concept: Casa Editrice Bonechi
Publication Manager: Monica Bonechi
Picture research: Editorial Staff
Graphics and layout: Monica Bonechi, Serena de Leonardis, Sonia Gottardo
Make-up: Patrizia Fabbri - *Cover:* Sonia Gottardo
Editing: Patrizia Fabbri

© Copyright by Casa Editrice Bonechi, Via Cairoli 18/b – Florence – Italy
E-mail: bonechi@bonechi.it

*The photographs are the property of the Casa Editrice Bonechi Archives.
Other contributors:*
Ina Agency Press: *pages 9, 10/11, 14, 15, 31 below, 38 above and below,
39 centre right and below, 40 below, 45.*
NordicPhotos / IMS Bildbyrå / Mira Bildarkiv: *page 39 above.*
Courtesy of Papermark:
*photos pages 17, 21, 24/25, 34 below left (by Jari Halminen);
photos pages 1, 6, 7, 16, 20/21, 23 centre, 26, 27, 29 above and centre left,
30, 31 above, 33 above, centre and below left, 34 above and below right, 35,
39 below left, 40/41, 41 third photo from top, 42, 43 above, 44/45
(by Markku Wiik);
photos pages 3, 4/5, 8, 12, 13, 18, 19, 22/23, 23 below, 26/27, 28,
29 centre and below right and left, 33 below right, 36/37, 41 all photos
except third from top (by Arto Komulainen);
photo pages 43 below (by Esko Parssinen).*

*The publisher will be grateful for information concerning the sources of
photographs without credits and will be pleased to acknowledge them
in future editions.*

ISBN 978-88-476-1852-7
Internet: www.bonechi.com

A   10   9   8   7   6   5   4   3   2   1

INTRODUCTION

The Arctic Circle, with the thousands of associations which the name evokes, even among those who have never set foot there, is the southernmost part of Lapland. This region of Finland therefore has every claim to represent the myth of the "Far Frozen North", as popular with tourists as myths of the Orient or Africa. Here, visitors come to admire the extraordinary hues of the midnight sun in the summer, or in winter to peer out from the protective warmth of a *Sami* tent in the midst of the snow at the rarefied light of the *kaamos*, the characteristic polar night illuminated from time to time by the brush-strokes of the breathtaking aurora borealis. Lapland is a frontier region.
One immediately feels this on arrival at **Enontekiö**, the little airport in the north-western part of the region. It is a little white and blue building in the middle of nowhere, where the birch and pine woods have already given way some distance back to soft rounded hills, *tunturi*, covered with lichen and musk, the last representatives of a flora which soon will have to give way to the ice and freezing ferocity of a winter which may last as long as nine months.
In fact, he landscape of Lapland is not made up of snow-covered peaks, or imposing glaciers or dizzy heights; on the contrary, it is quite flat, stretching out over the interminable reaches of the typical Arctic tundra, where only here and there some daring birch tree manages to assert itself. It is interrupted only by rivers or lakes, frozen over in the winter.
The highest peaks reach just over 3000 feet, and are mainly found in the areas bordering Sweden and Norway. The highest is *Haltiatunturi* (1328 m.), followed by *Saanatunturi* (1029 m.).
In such an environment, which to many seems hostile and difficult, the reindeer is the undisputed ruler.

Almost two hundred thousand of them live in this land, and they provide an inexhaustible source of sustenance for the inhabitants, who number about the same. Almost everything belonging to the reindeer is used – from the pelt to the antlers to the meat – and a visit to **Torassieppi** is enough to make this clear. Here we can learn about the moments of greatest significance in the life of the herd – the birth of the young, branding, separation and slaughter, but also by reflection the life that is lived by this unique people, the Lapps.

A section of this people belongs more properly to the ethnic group of the Sami, a Nordic population characterised by their colourful clothes of blue cloth, decorated in red and yellow; they also wear strange breeches with stitching made out of reindeer skin, and a tall hat decorated with coloured ribbons.

The Nordic Sami population consists of around seventy thousand people, of whom about 6500 live in Finnish Lapland. They occupy the territory divided between Norway, Sweden, Russia and Finland. Almost all of them are united by their common language, *Sami*, which has several dialects, and by a culture and tradition which are both unique in the world.

The tundra and forests, unequivocal kingdom of the reindeer, are the most classic elements of a typical landscape in Finnish Lapland.

LAPLAND'S NATIONAL PARKS

Finland's National Parks are protected areas where nature has remained untouched, as far as possible, and one can enjoy it to the full provided one shows equal respect for it by following the rules of behaviour which safeguard it. Only in this way will we be able to know and understand the deep sentiments of love, respect and gratitude which the Finns have for nature, an inexhaustible source of joy and serenity.

In the southernmost part of Lapland, near *Kemijärvi*, one of the four great national parks of this region has been created: the **National Park of Pyhätunturi**, which includes part of the Finnish mountain chain culminating in the peaks known as *Pyhä* and *Luosto*. It is characterised by steep cliffs, profound gorges and rocky surfaces. There is a visitors' centre in the park, and many routes for trekking are indicated. One of the most attractive routes is the deep gorge of *Pyhäkuru*, which cuts between the two peaks o *Kultakero* and *Ukonhattu*.

The **Urho Kekkonen National Park**, dedicated to th President of Finland who consolidated Finland's positio on the international scene, extends for about 2550 squar kilometres in the area from Saariselkä (the park is als known by this name) to the huge forests where the rive Nuorttijoki flows, to the east. Given the huge extent of th territory covered by the park, it is possible to find ever kind of flora and fauna there, making it a truly uniqu site. It is possible to stay overnight in some of the refuge and the Information Centre for the park is to be found i **Tankavaara**.

The largest park in Lapland, and indeed in the whole o Finland, is the **Lemmenjoki Park**, with 2855 square kilo metres of wild sub-Arctic conifer and birch forest, bar rounded hills, rivers and marshes. The main attraction i the valley of the river which gives its name to the Park. Her too it is possible to make use of a Visitors' Centre to lear

more about specific features of the area and to find the best camping-sites.

The other park in Lapland is the **Pallas-Ounastunturi Park**, situated on a chain of hills at the foot of which the vegetation is the typical conifer forest surrounded by peat. Here too there is a very well-equipped Visitors' Centre, and you can camp or spend the night at places indicated by the Park Management.

As we head north we find many other small towns, and beauty spots along the wide roads which cut through this distinctive Nordic countryside, characterised by low mountains (*tunturi*), clear streams, unusual vegetation and a few sizeable lakes in the most northerly area. In the south-east of Lapland there are lakes, like **Kemijärvi**, which abound in fish, and fast-flowing rivers which converge in this part of the region, forming thirty rapids. This makes it an ideal spot for those who enjoy rafting.

Armed with large sieves, amateur gold seekers patiently sift the waters of rivers near Tankavaara in search of possible treasure.

GOLD

In **Tankavaara**, situated near the park, many people are seized with gold fever in the summer season. By paying an entry-ticket to the gold-seeking area, it is possible to have a try at sifting a little gold from the river sand. All you need is a handy receptacle, a lot of patience, and a certain amount of luck! Every year there is a gold-seekers' competition, and the winner is named champion of the craft.

In the village the **Golden World** exhibition was opened in June 1995. The story of the discovery of gold in more than 20 countries of the world is on display here.

The amazing kaleidoscope of colours that nature offers during the various seasons of the year are only one of the numerous attractions of the great Finnish National Parks.

Noted for the stylish buildings that stand out impressively with their skillful illumination, Rovaniemi is the elegant result of the imagination of Alvar Aalto, an architectural genius who was also responsible for the futuristic bridge across the Ounasjoki river and the unmistakable form of the Arktikum Centre (above).

ROVANIEMI

Rovaniemi is the capital and the main port of access to Finnish Lapland. It is a small town on the river Ounasjoki, and is quite modern, since, after being destroyed by the German troops in the second World War, it was rebuilt following an urban plan created by Alvar Aalto.
The **Lutheran Church** in the town is worth a visit; it has an unusual fresco in the interior of the apse, showing Christ surrounded by Lapp people, with the whole scene portrayed in a typical Nordic setting.
The architectural complex which Aalto also designed for the Municipal Theatre and the City Congress Centre is most attractive. Known as the **Lappia talo**, it was built in 1975. A **library** is attached to it, with a collection of 500,000 volumes, the most ancient of which dates back to 1561 and

is written in Italian. The **City Hall** is also part of the complex designed by Aalto.
Another of the town's attractions is the unusual **Arktikum Centre**, inaugurated in 1992. This is a long glass tunnel facing northwards, which delves into the depths of the earth, almost as if to signify the profound links of this people with nature. The **Lapland Museum** which is housed here is the best way to satisfy the visitor's curiosity about this land and its people; in 1994 it was awarded a prize as the best Museum in Europe. The Arktikum Centre also houses an institute involved with research into the people and the nature of the Arctic zones, and the results of this research are presented to the public in both permanent exhibits and various short-term exhibitions held in the Centre.

Alvar Aalto
(Kuortane, 1898 - Helsinki, 1976)

One of modern Finland's most famous personalities is without doubt Alvar Aalto, a supreme architect as well as designer and town planner. He knew how to combine perfectly the most abstract requirements of pure functionality with the more fundamental aspects of constant daily use. He designed many architectural works in his homeland, perfectly in harmony with the environment yet entirely functional, but he was also responsible for buildings of international importance (such as the Finnish Pavilions designed for the Paris exhibition in 1937) which confirmed him as one of the most acclaimed personalities on the architectural scene worldwide. Now considered as one of the fathers of contemporary architecture, Aalto died in Helsinki in May 1976.

IN THE ARCTIC CIRCLE

Close to Rovaniemi passes the boundary of the **Arctic Circle** (*Napapiiri*), the imaginary line that indicates the southernmost point in Finland at which the midnight sun can be observed. Santa Claus has his headquarters there in *Santa Claus Village* and every year thousands of children address their Christmas present lists to the village post office. **Father Christmas** sends a reply to every one of them (supposed that he has got clear and readable addresses) in a letter personalized with his own special stamp. An enchanted world of snow and ice lies all around creating the magical atmosphere associated with this famous character, while the incomparable wonder of the magnificent northern light explodes in a kaleidoscope created by the **aurora borealis** and **midnight suns**.

THE NORTHERN LIGHTS

While it might be true that in the popular imagination the far north is usually associated with lengthy periods of cold and dark, it is also undeniable that one of the most fascinating aspects of Lapland is not only the beautiful, amazingly crisp and clear, quality of the daylight but also the unusual display of lights, typical of the Arctic night. Everyone has heard of the fascinating aurora borealis, an unique optical phenomenon of the northern hemisphere, created by the appearance of lights in the night sky, sometimes accompanied by a low noise. This is caused by the solar wind which, trapped in the earth's magnetic field, accumulates in the Van Allen belts and is then released into the atmosphere producing these magical light effects. And that is not all – the mythical midnight sun is another phenomenon visible north of the Arctic Circle (latitude 66° 23') during the summer period when the sun remains above the horizon all night creating a continual day with suffused, soft light that is impossible to imagine for those who have never seen it.

Naturally, however, in winter the diametrically opposite phenomenon occurs and it is the polar night and its dense darkness that dominates for most of the season.

Santa Claus
Village

SANTAPARK

Situated in the province of Rovaniemi, excavated in the depths of the *Syväsenvaara hill*, it's the Santapark, where you can enjoy the atmosphere of Christmas all year round. Together with Father Christmas, his elves and reindeer, this park offers a unique and unforgettable experience.

Dear Santa ...

F̃inland is the birthplace of Santa Claus, also known as Father Christmas. But have you ever wondered how old that generous old fellow dressed in red and sporting those white whiskers must be? According to some rumours, he's getting on for 500 years old, and he spends the best part of the year in the heart of Finnish Lapland, at Korvatunturi, where his innumerable helpers, the elves, make it possible for him to deal with the thousands of requests for presents which arrive, full of expectation, from all over the world. Korvatunturi, in the district of Savukoski, has about 2000 inhabitants and about 20,000 reindeer, apart from those belonging to Santa, of course.

As it is rather an out-of-the-way place, Santa Claus also has a workshop, with a lot of sleighs and reindeer, and his own personal post office near Rovaniemi, exactly where the Arctic Circle lies.

In his period of greatest activity - Christmas Eve - Santa Claus goes off with his sack overflowing with presents to almost every house in Finland; he knocks at the door, and asks how the children of the house have been behaving ... generally the children win his heart by singing a special little song, and finally the much-awaited present is delivered without further delay.

You want to know his address? Here it is:
Santa Claus
Arctic Polar Circle
96930 Rovaniemi, Finland

LAPLAND BETWEEN SWEDEN AND NORWAY

The city of **Tornio** in Finnish Lapland is really coupled with the Swedish city of **Haparanda**, but although there is a boundary between them on the map, in reality they form a single city, each part closely linked to the other.

Tornio has one of the most beautiful wooden churches in Finland, dating from 1686, but the main attractions of the town are its setting and its sporting facilities. Just one example of these: the city's great **Kukkolankoski Rapids**. These are more than three kilometres long, and the difference in level is around 14 metres. Every year the spectacular *Arctic Canoeing Regatta* is held on these rapids.

One curious feature is that the *Green Zone* Golf Course has its eighteen holes divided across Finland and Sweden, between which there is a time difference of an hour!

Heading North again, we come to the city of **Ylitornio**, again on the border with Sweden, which also has its Swedish twin, **Övertorneå**. The city is a well-known tourist resort, since it stands near the **Aavasaksa** mountains, on the summit of which the traditional *Midsummer Night's Festival* is held at the end of June each year.

Another village on the Swedish border is **Pello**, situated on the banks of the river which marks the actual frontier: on the other bank is the Swedish twin town, to which Pello is joined by a bridge. The name of Pello is associate above all with salmon fishing, and with the *Poikkinain Festival*, which takes place every July and celebrates ma riages that take place across the frontier with great fe tivities. Every year there is an actual marriage ceremor in the middle of the town's river, followed by tradition singing and dancing.

The village of **Kolari**, hidden away in the typical Nord landscape of the border country, and the last railway st. tion in the north of Finland, is near the winter sports cent of **Ylläs Tunturi**, 718 metres high, where the longest dow ward ski-slopes of Finland are found.

Near here there is another place sacred to the Lapp **Pakasaivo**, the "Lapland Hell", where the ancestors present-day Lapps used to make sacrifices to their deitie It is a lake hidden away in a forest, the surface of which around 50 metres below ground level.

Further north again is **Muonio**, where a short walk acro the *Muonionjoki Bridge* brings one into Sweden. The ci was already inhabited during the Stone Age, and today it a focal point for the whole area of north-eastern Laplan The wooden **Church** was designed in 1817 by an Itali architect, Carlo Bassi. Close at hand is the beautiful *La Jerisjärvi*, where some fishermen's cottages dating from t eighteenth century are still in a good state of preservatio Sweden can also be reached very easily from the village **Kaaresuvanto** and its twin town, **Karesuando**. From bo

Luxuriant and unspoiled nature entirely dominates the slopes of the Aavasaksa fells.

villages it is possible to see the midnight sun from the middle of July onwards.

Kilpisjärvi, on the lake of the same name, is the first village that one meets with in the triple frontier area between Sweden, Norway and Finland. From the city, *Mount Saana* can be seen, more than 1000 metres high, and surrounded by magnificent countryside. Another frontier town between Norway and Finland is **Karigasniemi**, on the *river Tenojoki*. The whole area is a mythical zone for the Lapps, and the view from nearby *Mount Ailigas* is absolutely superb.

Again on the Norwegian border, we find **Utsjoki**, the major attraction of which is the **Kevo Canyon**, 40 kilometres in length. The most beautiful part of the gorge is where the *river Kevojoki* opens into the long and narrow *Lake Njaggaljärvi*, a scene which can only be reached by foot, but is every bit worth the effort.

...ello, a typical little village surrounded y vegetation and with many traditional uildings, is situated on the banks of the river ornionjoki which marks the border with eighbouring Sweden.

SKI RESORTS

Almost nowhere in the world are the conditions for skiing so favourable as they are in Finland.

The very long skiing season in northern Finland begins in October and lasts at least until the middle of May. Almost all the winter sports centres have floodlit cross-country tracks and downhill slopes to extend the day's skiing.

Apart from the numerous cross-country tracks and downhill slopes, Finnish ski resorts also provide a vast range of other winter activities, including snow boarding, snowmobile safaris, and dog- or reindeer-pulled sleigh rides. Moreover, Finnish ski schools are well-known and highly-thought of at international level.

One of the most popular and famous ski resorts in Lapland is **Ylläs**, the largest skiing centre in the Arctic icecap.

The cross-country tracks which branch out from here lead to other important winter sports centres, such as **Levi**, **Muonio** and **Hetta**, or cross the lonely landscape of Western Lapland, creating a network of tracks which extends for almost 1000 km!

Saariselkä, on the edge of the **UKK National Park**, is one of the best-loved winter sports centres in Finland and is also ideal as a departure point for ski trips lasting several days.

Pyhä, close to the **Pyhätunturi National Park**, is the favourite destination of expert skiers. From here it is possible to visit the park on skis and ski the famous track which links *"tunturi Pyhä"* and **Luosto**.

Views from the very heart of Finnish Lapland: the two famous ski resorts of Ylläs (photos centre and below) and Levi (photos on the left and above).

Typical architecture of this region where tradition lives in perfect harmony with modernity: Utsjoki with the futuristic bridge across a broad section of the river with the same name and, right, from the top, Muonio, Enontekiö and two views of Kolari.

FISHING

Since fish (from salmon to trout, or pike and bass) has always been one of the staple foods in the diet of Laplanders, it is hardly surprising that fishing is one of the most common sporting activities, particularly in the lakes and rivers but also on the brief coastal areas of this wild region where the waters are just teeming with fish. Indeed, it is no exaggeration to say that fishing, especially fresh water, is a real national sport and is not to be discouraged even when thick ice dominates the landscape (holes have then to be cut in it to reach the water below). Moreover, with such magnificent, unique and natural surroundings, the sport is attracting an increasing number of tourists who come to fish, though they must hold an official permit to do so.

KUUSAMO

This small town, formed by scattered groups of stylish modern houses, owes its fame principally to the surrounding countryside and the spectacular resources that it offers. Just a short climb to the top of **Mount Livaara** (little more than a hill at 471 metres height) reveals a sweeping panorama of lakes, tundra and forests. Here, almost on the border with Russia, we get an instant impression of Lapland. The nearby **Oulanka National Park**, dedicated to this wonderful landscape, is famous for some fascinating trekking

Kuusamo, with its characteristic scattered houses and modern buildings surrounded by plants and trees, is a true gateway into Lapland.

routes (such as the renowned **Bear Trail**), its wealth of flora, (including moreover, a unique native orchid) and the spectacular *rapids* within the park. In fact numerous rivers rush swiftly around Kuusamo and provide a real paradise for fishing enthusiasts with abundant catches, amongst which are the rare brown trout that arrive here from nearby Russia.

Even wintertime in Kuusamo and its environs offers excellent resources, with high quality infrastructures available for those who enjoy winter sports of any kind whatever. Twenty six kilometres further north, **Ruka** is the absolute showpiece of the entire area. Lying at the foot of **Rukatunturi**, a mount of about 462 metres, this well-known ski resort boasts all the most modern equipment and one can enjoy downhill skiing and ski jumping, try out exciting slopes or improve one's techniques at one of the local skiing schools.

Perfect snow on the slopes that are lit when dusk begins to fall, modern jumps, spectacular cross country ski routes – Ruka offers winter sports enthusiasts absolutely first rate facilities.

SPORT

One of the greatest secrets of the quite unique fascination of Finnish Lapland is without doubt its spectacular and unspoilt countryside where nature has remained untamed. The region is therefore quite ideal for open-air sports and also offers truly memorable excursions. It is no surprise therefore that Lapland is universally accepted as one of the best areas in Europe for trekking, with its endless itineraries across the Arctic tundra, where the vegetation is mainly shrubs and lichens, leading to forests where it is not unusual to meet – apart from the classic reindeer – bears and wolves, foxes and elks, hares and wood grouse. The abundant waters of the crystal rivers are ideal for downstream canoeing and enthusiasts of whitewater rafting can also enjoy them in dinghies. And if hunting and fishing are not for you, don't forget that once the snow falls, the vast stretches of Lapland become a veritable paradise for lovers of all kinds of winter sport.

THE CENTRE OF LAPP CULTURE AND TRADITION

At the end of March, at **Hetta** in the north-west of Lapland, there is the annual *Feast of Mary*, the most important event in which the Sami community takes part. For two days, the little town, no more than a few houses scattered around a chapel, is enlivened by stalls, handicrafts, hats, gloves, boots made from suede or leather, axes, lassoes for the reindeer, and so on. The fair is attended by the Sami, who come to the town to take part in the competitions held there; for the occasion they wear their bright traditional blue and red costume.

The key events of the festival are the traditional reindeer race, and especially the reindeer-catching rodeo, using lassoes – a real test of skill among the breed-ers. At the moment there are 42 communities herding reindeer, which represent the principal resource of Lapland, apart from tourism. There are two special occasions each year in which the reindeer are rounded up by the breeders: the first in the period around St John's Day, for branding the animals, a marking operation which is still done by hand, and involves the incision in the animal's ear of a special mark which is the "brand". The second herding event is in November, for the slaughter.

In the wild territories of north-eastern Lapland too, there are plenty of examples of the many-faceted culture and original workmanship of the Lapps. In **Posio** we can find the products of Lapp-style ceramic work. Traditional forms and colours have today merged with more modern designs, giving rise to completely original works. The small town of **Salla**, on the other hand, is completely dedicated to the reindeer and its associations. Here there is the **Reindeer Park** (*Poropuisto*) where a

economic activities linked to the animal are exhaustively portrayed – and it is also possible to go for a ride on a reindeer.

Among the most interesting places from the point of view of local handicrafts is **Kemijärvi**, the last fair-sized town in northern Finland. It is here that the real Sami territory begins, and this is the entrance to the territory famous for its gold-seeking and for the renowned **Arctic Route**, which thousands of Europeans travel every year in order to reach the **Nordkapp**, the northernmost point of the continent of Europe. Every year there are various events, among them the **International Week of Sculpture**, in which Lapp and foreign artists take part. The goods produced in the previous year are exhibited on a permanent basis.

The town of **Sodankylä**, already a gathering point for the Lapps in the sixteenth century, is important from the point of view of Lapp art; one of its most important exponents is **Andrea Alariesto**, whose paintings are displayed in the gallery bearing his name. The city is also well-known because in June the International Cinema event known as the *Midnight Sun Film Festival* is held there.

Aki Kaurismäki
(Orimattila, 4 April 1957)

The films of Aki Kaurismäki, the best-known Finnish cinema director, portray the very poorest of social strata and situations, mainly in Northern Europe and often using extreme characters and environments. With his brother, **Mika**, he founded the *Midnight Sun Film Festival* in Sodankylä and the distribution company "Ville Alpha" named after the film *Alphaville* by Jean-Luc Godard. In 2002 his film *The Man without a Past* was a prize winner at the Cannes Film Festival.

Kittilä (above) and Posio – the unmistakable linear simplicity of the architecture and the magnificent natural environment make these towns the true homeland of Lapp culture and traditions.

However, the most popular Lapp painter is certainly **Reidar Särestöniemi**. His birthplace is in **Kittilä** and it has been transformed into a museum. The most striking feature of his paintings is the uniqueness and vivid colours of the northern landscape, which seem almost to emerge from the paintings and enwrap us.

In early September a marathon is also held in this little town; since it is organised each year, it is probably the most northerly annual event in the world.

As we continue to head north, not far from the village of **Pokka**, on *Lake Taatsi*, a great rock in the form of a column can be seen. Known as the **Taatsin seita**, it was considered a sacred place by the Sami people, a kind of dwelling-place for their gods.

Inari, with its seventeen thousand square kilometres, is the largest municipal area in Finland, but also the least densely inhabited. It is also the real heartland of Lapp culture. Here and at **Sevettijärvi**, the village which faces on to the northern shores of the lake, about two thousand Lapps live, five hundred of whom belong to the *Skolt* ethnic group, of Orthodox religion, who until 1944 lived in the city of Petsamo, which now belongs to Russia. They speak three languages, Russian and *Skolt*, as well as Finnish.

In Inari one can visit the **Sami Open Air Museum**, which provides a broad over-view of the culture and way of life of this ethnic group. In a thick pine forest, the last permanent homes of the Lapps that remained standing after the second world war have been collected together, and here it is possible to find craft goods with typical *Sami* decoration, hand-made using materials gathered directly from nature and especially from the reindeer. Traditional costumes and hunting and fishing implements are also on display.

Another important meeting-point for the Sami is the **Erämaakirkko** near *Lake Pielpajärvi*, seven kilometres from Inari. The atmosphere which surrounds this church, in the midst of the wild Lapland countryside, is of quiet solemnity. The area around the church has been a point of exchange and trade over the centuries for these people who have held their market there since the first church was built in 1646. The present building dates from 1760, and a number of subsequent restorations have returned the paintings near the pulpit to their original splendour.

Lake Inari, with its three thousand islands, is another important site for the Sami. The **Island of Ukko** (or *Ajjih* in the *Sami* language) can be reached by boat; it has been a sanctuary for at least a thousand years.

A characteristic image of the famous Sami Open Air Museum in northern Inari.

THE REINDEER

There are many reindeer in Finland. The herds of this placid mammal prefer the tundra of Lapland, where they find plenty of lichen, though when necessary they will also eat mushrooms and birch and willow shoots.

The reindeer herds live in the wild state, but they are herded into large, specially built corrals twice a year by the Lapp herdsmen, for the operation of branding the young, and for slaughter. The reindeer is the principal source of sustenance, apart from tourism, for these people: since they are so valuable, every breeder recognises his own deer on sight, simply by looking at their ears. All the deer of a herd have a recognition mark, which consists of an incision in the ear. Each individual breeder or cooperative of breeders has his or its own individual mark, and is capable of recognising it from some 16,000 others.

In November the deer are again herded in by the breeders for slaughter: in general, it is the males that have reached more than one year old, and the oldest females, who are slaughtered for meat and pelts. In order to find food in the winter, the reindeer move down to the great conifer forests south of Lapland, where the layer of snow covering the plants on which they feed is thinner. But in the summer they return northward, and settle in the tundra where the danger from mosquitoes and flies to the newly-born deer is reduced. In Finland there are also some wild reindeer, the *Rangifer tarandus fennicus*. The small number still remaining live mostly in the northernmost part of the country and of Russia, but recently the central-western territory in the area of **Reisjärvi** and **Perho** has been successfully repopulated.

THE SIBERIAN JAY – KUUKKELI

Despite the very hard climate during most of the year, one of the animals that never leaves the territories of Lapland – and as a permanent inhabitant is almost a symbol of the area – is this pretty little bird, not unlike a large sparrow (about 30 cm.). It passes the winter sleeping in the hollow trunks of trees and spends about 3-4 hours a day in a frenetic search for food. In the warmer and less difficult months, its diet is more varied and abundant as it enjoys seeds pecked directly out of pine cones, and also appreciates other foods and seeds such as small mushrooms and insects, and even some fish. The female lays the eggs quite early in a nest lined with feathers and moss set high up in the warm shelter of a tree. In fact, the young have to learn to fly quickly for winter arrives early in Lapland.

A MAN, A SLEIGH AND A DOG

Living in extreme Arctic latitudes has never been easy for humans.
Travelling and manoeuvering through snow and ice in absolute solitude has always been a complex operation. The only solution is a sleigh and these faith-

ful travelling companions – the packs of tireless sleigh dogs (Samoyed, Husky, and Alaskan Malamute) that are distant relations of the Arctic wolf, capable of withstanding the cold, fatigue and long periods of travel over great distances, they are obedient and lively, loyal to their owners but entirely and instinctively pack animals.

THE SAMI

The *Sami* people have inhabited Lapland for ever. With their brightly coloured – and warm – clothing and tenacity they have successfully challenged the long winters and freezing Arctic winds for millennia. They are nomads by calling and by choice, and are zealous of their ancient traditions that include a unique language and culture, craftwork and quite singular mythology. And they share their lives with their wonderful sleigh dogs. The Sami have just one, precious and irreplaceable resource: reindeer – their priceless wealth.

The *Sami* language is made up of three dialects of Finno-Ugric origin. In order to preserve and promote the *Sami* language and culture, the Scandinavian countries founded the Sami Parliament in 1973,

while the Nordic Council of the Sami was established in 1956; as a consequence of this cultural and political development, the *Sami* language is now accepted as a legal language in schools and courts.

With the rigours of long winters, the precarious nature of a traditionally nomadic life, a tough lifestyle, most frugal shelters, the existence of the Sami people may seem full of difficulties, yet they maintain very strong ties with their age-old customs. They live in harmony with untamed nature and their most loyal companions, the reindeer – their only real wealth. Originally raised for meat, today they are also a fascinating tourist attraction, providing a new and precious economic resource for this ancient and fascinating people, whose identity also lies in their own language (opposite page, centre).

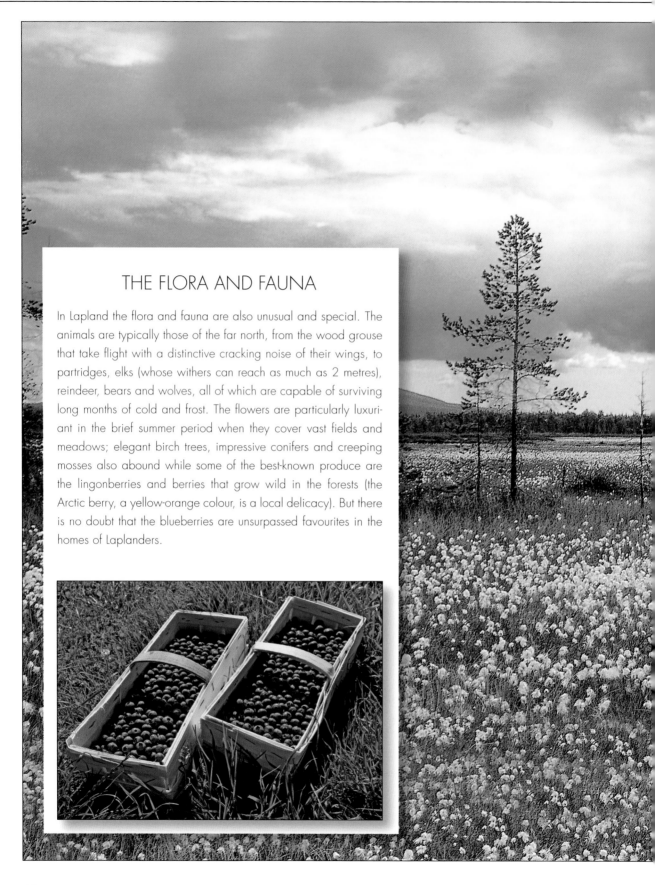

THE FLORA AND FAUNA

In Lapland the flora and fauna are also unusual and special. The animals are typically those of the far north, from the wood grouse that take flight with a distinctive cracking noise of their wings, to partridges, elks (whose withers can reach as much as 2 metres), reindeer, bears and wolves, all of which are capable of surviving long months of cold and frost. The flowers are particularly luxuriant in the brief summer period when they cover vast fields and meadows; elegant birch trees, impressive conifers and creeping mosses also abound while some of the best-known produce are the lingonberries and berries that grow wild in the forests (the Arctic berry, a yellow-orange colour, is a local delicacy). But there is no doubt that the blueberries are unsurpassed favourites in the homes of Laplanders.

THE FAR NORTH

The road towards the extreme north and the northern-most border between Finnish Lapland and the Norwegian territories is the lengthy *4-E75* – the famous *Arctic Route*. Passing through **Sodankylä**, **Saariselkä**, **Ivalo**, **Inari**, on as far as **Utsjoki**, it continues right up to the legendary *North Cape*. Along the way, towns and isolated villages appear steeped in tradition, yet also quite open to modernity. For many months of the year they are affected by the rigours of winter. In fact, the frozen Arctic Sea is not so far away and the *Lake of Inari*, the second largest in Finland, is linked directly to it by the *Paatsjoki*.

Opposite page, from top and from right; views of the far north along the Arctic Route: Ivalo, two views of Saariselkä, Ivalo again (showing the Lutheran Church with its modern metal façade built in 1965), Utsjoki and Kultala.

This page, more views of the area around Utsjoki where the scenery is of lakes, tundra, forests and endless wild beauty.

THE SAUNA

A tradition whose origins are now lost in the far and distant past (the vapour is considered to be purifying energy as in a veritable religious rite), today the sauna is a truly enjoyable and invigorating daily ritual for the Finnish.

The real sauna of the Lapps, however, takes place in a special structure where stones are heated on a fire of pine and birch branches and hot and cold water is poured on them, immediately creating steam while a perfumed smoke arises from the fire. Bundles of birch twigs are used to stimulate the circulation by beating the perspiring body. For half an hour, at regular intervals, more water is poured on the stones creating more steam and vapour.

To fully invigorate skin and body the sauna ends with a cold shower – and even better if possible, a plunge into the cold water of a nearby lake.

FOOD AND COOKERY IN LAPLAND

For centuries Finnish cooking in general and Lapp in particular, was entirely dictated by the resources and limitations of northern lands with their difficult environment and unfavourable climate. Thus, although today it is possible to import the most varied requirements and satisfy the most demanding of palates, local traditions are faithfully respected and proudly defended.

There are many deliciously flavoured soups and meat dishes based on reindeer meat, casseroled or stewed together with onions and mushrooms (from porcini to chanterelle and russula) found in quantity during the summer months in the forests. Hare is also popular in Lapp cooking, as well as elk (usually roast), snow grouse and willow grouse. Also abundantly available is delicious local fish – salmon and trout, whitefish and arctic charr, not to mention a great variety of fresh water fish, cooked in a variety of ways. A rare delicacy, as they are so briefly available, are the highly popular river prawns, best eaten steamed. As well as mushrooms, the woods provide an incredible variety of berries, cleverly used in sauces, salads and as accompaniments.

Cheeses are also delicious, both soft and mature, including the famous *leipäjuusto* a genuine speciality of Lapland. And to end the meal, delicious berries (raspberries, strawberries and blueberries) are used in exquisite desserts, accompanied by tasty grappa and local vodka (wine, however, is imported). Interestingly, in Lapland

breakfast is quite abundant (with many different kinds of bread, including the unique Arctic bread, which is grey in colour and cooked on the gridle) while lunch is also generous; supper, though, is frugal with few and often cold dishes.

INDEX

Introduction ....Page 3

Lapland's National Parks ...." 6

Gold ...." 7

Rovaniemi ...." 9

Alvar Aalto ...." 9

In the Arctic Circle ...." 11

The northern lights ...." 13

Santapark ...." 14

Dear Santa ... ." 15

Lapland between Sweden and Norway ...." 16

Sky resorts ...." 19

Fishing ...." 23

Kuusamo ....Page 25

Sport ...." 29

The centre of Lapp culture
  and tradition ...." 30

Aki Kaurismäki ...." 31

The reindeer ...." 33

The Siberian Jay – Kuukkeli ...." 35

A man, a sleigh and a dog ...." 35

The Sami ...." 39

The flora and fauna ...." 40

The far north ...." 42

The sauna ...." 44

Food and cookery in Lapland ...." 46